The Great Before

Ross Clark was born in 1966. Since winning the Spectator Young Writers' Award in 1989 he has been a freelance journalist and regular contributor to the Spectator, the Times and the Sunday Telegraph. He is the author of the Pimlico county history of Cambridgeshire.

The Great Before
a satire

Ross Clark

www.greatbefore.com

First published by *www.greatbefore.com* 2005
20 Great Lane
Reach
Cambridge
CB5 0JF

www.greatbefore.com

ISBN 0 9551499 0 8

British Library Cataloguing-in-Publication Data
A Catalogue record for this book is available
from the British Library.

1

The Great Before

The Isle of Dogs
1 September 2051

I want to write to you as if I believed you had just been revived from forty years of cryogenic suspension. I know that is an unlikely feat. I am sure that the hopeful corpses lying in freezers awaiting cures for their diseases have long since thawed and the swells who earned fortunes from putting them there all by now gone to experience their own mortality. But I have a desire to leave my last letter to my own people. Our successors are a very different breed, and I am sorry that often I find it difficult to converse with them.

So let us say that early in the century you were horribly mangled in some road accident – a real martyr of the industrial age, you – and that, appalled by such a tragic loss and drunk on the promises of science, your family were moved to have you deep frozen in preparation for reincarnation when death had finally been defeated. Your people are long gone, but some miracle-worker up in the hills – for that is what he would now be called – has by some happy accident managed to rekindle the spark of life in you.

Sleeper, you are in for a nasty awakening. Those dewy eyelids of yours are flickering upon a world which you will not recognise. There are mornings when I, too, wake up to find myself in a strange land; the people, places and mentalities of my youth seem like a rich carpet which has been pulled from under me and I have been thrown backwards onto the cold stone floor that is old age. My only wish is that I might save your poor eyes from the worst by disclosing only gradually what has happened to us all while you slumbered.

Let me start with a little note about myself. My name is Matthew Gonne and next week I will be 85 years old, subject of course to me lasting that long. My physician has informed me that I shall live only until the first frosts, and already there is a nip in the air. This morning I awoke with a fine bonnet of dew upon my bald and pitted head; I am sleeping with my head close to a window which is furnished with only a few remnants of glass. It occurs to me that I ought to ask my nurse to turn me about, so that it is my feet which face windwards; that way I imagine I might gain a few extra days and thus have more time to finish my letter to you.

But enough of this miserable place. I want to take you back to the spring of this year, 2051, when I was living in an enviable position. I was then installed at Trinity College, that notable institution in Cambridge, where Sir Isaac Newton first conceived gravity and which as I am sure you remember boasts more Nobel prizes than France. And to think that of all this I was master!

It is a post to which, I ought to confess, I appointed myself in the year 2039 upon the death of the greater part of the fellowship in a virulent plague. I had had the good fortune to be out of residence at the time, to which I owe my survival. Upon becoming master, I also bestowed upon myself the title of Professor of Old Learning; an unfamiliar subject to you, I am sure, but one which I felt summed up my role in attempting to preserve various strands of human knowledge through very difficult times.

You will have gathered that the age in which you have just

awoken is a golden one for dilettantism. For the man of modest ability, it is a rewarding time to be alive. My scholars and I have been blessed with honours and distinctions which in any other age would have remained well above our station; we shine where once we might have seemed mere specks of humanity. There is a drawback, though, to this happy situation: there are relatively few people left on Earth to impress.

I must be careful in what I write, because I suspect you are already imagining great and terrible things. You have perhaps taken my reference to a reduced population as a sign that the world has succumbed to the apocalypse, and are now wondering which of those awful horsemen was responsible for the deed: war, famine, pestilence, tempest, or any of the other names which came to be bestowed upon the four riders. The answer is that none of them have contributed so much to our present condition as a previously uncredited fifth horseman: fear.

We do not use the word apocalypse; the most common way to describe the events of the past fifty years is the Rationalisation, a term which, you may recognise, was often used by the economists of your day, but which has now attained a religious significance. The Rationalisation, it is asserted, was God's work: a way of bringing back into line a world which was heading for doom. No matter the pain and suffering, it is a contention held by the majority that the events of the past half century were inevitable. Were it not for the Rationalisation, it is asserted, the world would by now be populated beyond the numbers it could safely sustain and would be polluted to levels beyond which the human body could tolerate. The Earth would be scorched, or otherwise drenched by deluge, and the air would be too thin to breathe. Any humans who remained would be unable to breed thanks to the residue of poisons. Better, then, that Man was put in his place by suffering a relatively modest correction in his fortunes than he was allowed to go on and extinguish himself altogether.

We have certainly seen our fair share of suffering; but please do not think of us as dazed and pitiful survivors of some terrible event. You have been carried away, perhaps, by those cheap and lurid volumes of science fiction, popular in your day, which foresaw us being consumed either by nuclear war, environmental disaster or else by technology run amok, but which forgot to give mankind due credit for the weaselly resilience with which he is able to withstand disasters of his own making. In the tale which I want to relate to you I am afraid that the demons all belong to Man himself; but then so, too, does the sheer stubbornness which has allowed him to survive, and in some cases to thrive.

It will take you some time to adjust to the nature of the world into which you have just awoken. I should begin by telling you that nowadays when we use the term 'the industrial age' we are referring to something which has been and gone. When we chance upon a colour photograph of the world as it was fifty years ago we look upon it as you would do upon an 18th century painting. There are things in it which we recognise, some things which we still possess, but what we cannot share is the mood. Whatever one thinks of the industrial age there is now an air of romanticism about it. It is hard to avoid thinking that the industrial era was a time when passions ran much hotter than they do now; when the thrill of being alive was so much greater. Only in my more lucid moments do I remember that then, as now, most of the people were engaged for most of the time in mundane affairs, matters relating to their immediate comfort. Thus they were in no position to tell that they were alive during what has come to be viewed as one of history's most remarkable and most tragic epochs.

When one brings up the subject of the industrial age these days it does not mean the same thing to all people. There are those who are pleased that it has passed, others who still inhabit it, using their memories as a shield against the realities of their life, and a few who fail to believe it has ever gone away. This latter group of people, you may find it hard to accept, are called 'modern' people.

The meaning of that word, you see, has been turned upside down: to say somebody is 'modern' is now a grave insult, denoting a person who has become out of touch, who denies the present because they would rather live in the past. A man damned as being modern is close in spirit to the man you would have called a reactionary; except that where your reactionary would perhaps have believed in manual work, the nation state, gothic architecture and rule by patricians, the modern man believes in electrical gadgetry, the United Nations, efficient plumbing and universal suffrage.

At best, the modern man is seen as a comic turn. More often, he is viewed as downright dangerous: a counter-revolutionary. This is because most people these days subscribe to a philosophy described as 'Progressive' thinking. This is another word whose meaning has changed. A 'Progressive' is one who believes that the future of mankind belongs to a bastardised form of feudalism. He maintains that man is a creature who was born to live on and to work the land. He does not travel, and regards outsiders with contempt. He believes, indeed, in 'Progress' – a term which has come to refer to a state of blissful, unchanging communion with the natural world; a state which is widely believed to have ruled the Earth before the advent of industrialisation. He considers the industrial age to have been an unhealthy interlude in history, and that now we have all simply returned to what we do best.

Few will stand up to the Progressives. The greater part of humanity is happy to go along with their strictures. Even those older people who remember the latter stages of the industrial age profess difficulty in remembering any good which came from them. Nor do the survivors of the industrial age like to admit to any memory of the knowledge and skills which existed at the time. You must forget now that old lie 'things cannot be disinvented'; they can and they are being. How to split an atom, how to engineer the genes of a plant; these things are rapidly being reduced to myth, mentioned occasionally in conversations in the taverns, to general head-shaking and disbelief. When shown a television or a computer and told what it could do, many people maintain that it was simply a device for sending the human mind into a trance; they believe that viewers did not see the pictures on the screen, but imagined them as a result of the radiation which was deliberately and mischievously beamed into their heads. What people will accept of the past depends much upon where they live. Those who reside on the eastern fringe of Cambridge look out upon the hulks of aeroplanes at the old airport and will tell you that they were killing machines built to carry off their passengers to their deaths. Many of those who live out of sight of the airport, on the other hand, refuse to accept the existence of aeroplanes at all. 'It is a lovely idea, the thought of being picked up by a machine and deposited far away,' one young fellow told me, laughing. 'But these planes are the product of over-active imaginations. If they had existed as you say, with great engines sucking the air from the sky, they would have left us nothing to breathe'.

Perhaps it is inevitable that people should refuse to believe in machinery: even in your day ordinary people did not understand how much of it worked. Part of the tragedy of the late industrial age is that human knowledge reached a stage which the masses found incomprehensible, and thus they felt alienated. It might be said that the masses have reclaimed for themselves a world which they can understand.

To conform with Progressive thinking, you must live a life which is parochial – a word which can be used quite literally because the parish has once again become an active unit of administration. The title 'Chairman of the Parish Council', which in your day was usually held by a harmless old buffoon, now instills fear in parishioners for it denotes a functionary of considerable power. In the hierarchy of rural England there is just one rank above Chairman of the Parish Council, and that is Lord of the Manor. Do not make the mistake of imagining this to be a person of high-breeding: a Lord of the Manor is the sort of figure you would more likely have called a lout, a yobbo, or at very best an entrepreneur. Our Lord in Cambridge, a bilious man by the name of Julius Holder, began his career as a second-hand car dealer. When his business was at a peak he bought himself the then redundant feudal title of 'Lord of the Manor' of one of the villages of Cambridgeshire, as a sop to his vanity. When it became clear to him that selling cars was no longer a viable business, he managed to convince local folk that his title still conferred powers upon its owner. Whenever a landowner died without issue, or an agricultural concern collapsed, Julius Holder appropriated the abandoned land. In this way, he built an empire surrounding the City of Cambridge. Consequently, he became a very powerful man, for land has become once again the most prized possession; and one over which men will happily kill another.

Industrial plant and manufactured goods, by contrast, count for very little in the present world. A certain amount of roughened manufacturing goes on – there is always a demand for shoes, as these items quickly wear out with the amount of walking a man must now undertake in his day-to-day life. But there is a vast surplus of goods left over from the industrial age which people are still happily working their way through. Markets abound with cheap goods which have been salvaged from old warehouses and which for the most part are still in good condition. Few people go about in rags, though I am afraid you will not find their dress stylish: they mix and match their styles and their colours at whim, so that it is not at all unusual to see people wearing a double-breasted jacket with the lower half of a nylon tracksuit. Most popular of all are those clothes which have weathered best: shell suits, anoraks, anything made with artificial fibres. Progressives frown upon such leftovers of the industrial age, preferring instead to wear hand-stitched garments, but most people wear the old clothes anyway.

It is in the gathering of food, and to a lesser extent the

cultivation of it, which provides the greatest employment these days. It will perhaps seem charming to you, the sight of gaunt figures trooping out into the fen to trap birds and frogs or venturing onto the clayey heaths to dig up the sugar beet and potatoes which grow there; these crops having spontaneously taken root at the end of the industrial age. They often sing as they go about their work, these food-gathering parties, reciting pop tunes of long ago whose words have become corrupted to the point of meaninglessness. They tell each other tales, strip off and dive into muddy pools to cool themselves down, eat for lunch turnips pulled straight from the ground, dirt dribbling from their chins. The diet of people in Cambridge is monotonous, and at times of the year food is in short supply; during late winter, in particular, people regularly fast to conserve what little they have. But they think their food good, and that they are privileged to eat so well. They exchange stories, in horror, of the food of the industrial age: the salty, fatty snacks in shrink-wrapped plastic which they blame for the feebleness of the elderly. Why, they say, if you look at the ancient churches with their great doorways and compare them with the doorways of industrial age buildings it is obvious that people of the pre-industrial age must have been well-nourished giants compared with the flatulent, emaciated people fed on junk food during the industrial age. The long-extinct manufacturers of junk food are reviled for the harm they wrought upon humanity. Once a year, on the day you knew as Christmas Day but which has become a day of solemn worship, the people of Cambridge show their disgust at the eating habits of the industrial age by manufacturing a large oval-shaped 'burger' from offal and general rubbish, which they then drag around the streets. They urinate and defecate upon it before finally burning it. When it has all gone to ashes, they cheer and say prayers, thankful that the unwholesome eating habits of the industrial age are no more. Then they repair for a simple supper of boiled turnip, washed down with a strong spirit brewed from sugar beet. That this makes them flatulent they blame upon poisons they believe to have been left in the soil by industrial age farmers. 'It's the nitrates,' they say as they clutch their bellies. 'There were nitrates in the food. I am so ill, and it is the fault of those industrial farmers!'

You are probably itching to get back to the industrial age. But I don't yet want to take you that far back; only to the early April of this year, 2051, when I was excited to receive a letter. This statement alone will require some explanation. It will be hard to impress upon you, who remember so freshly those piles of junk mail which used to land on your doormat, the pleasure which derives from the receiving of post. As Master of Trinity I received perhaps two letters a month. It was never a straightforward business. The postal service between Cambridge and the erstwhile Metropolis is intermittent. There is an heroic order of postmen who go about the business of keeping up communications with all the zeal of the early christians – and sometimes call themselves the Knights Postallers. But theirs is hazardous business. They are often picked upon by gangs of Progressive thugs, who see the postal service as an enemy of social order. Their life is one of dashing from safe house to safe house, seeking, by discreet enquiry, the people to whom their letters are addressed, hoping that they are not being led to the house of a Progressive, where they might be imprisoned or murdered. There are large profits to be made by delivering post, though many postmen and less motivated by the money than by their belief in the good of communication.

The word that a letter had arrived for me in the city of Cambridge would come to me via a casual word in the street. One of my staff would then be dispatched to collect it from a backstreet dwelling (no postman would risk walking up to our college gates). Eventually, I would receive an envelope with my name scrawled upon it, the words disguised as part of a drawing. Nobody would dare address an envelope these days in English. A certain amount of written language is still used: abbreviated words which have derived from the text-messaging of the late industrial age. But whole words and sentences, especially in printed form, are considered to be an evil. The Progressives point to the mass of literature left over from the industrial age, which few can now understand, and argue that the written language was a tool used in the suppression of ordinary people. People are easily convinced of this: the Progressives need only read a sentence from a scientific paper or a government document to entice a hostile response from those who cannot make out what was being written: 'what is this? It is the language of the devil!' Anyone caught writing other than in simple, abbreviated words is liable to be seized, put before a parish council and be forced to explain the meaning of their words. So, in order to write a letter it has become necessary to disguise words as parts of drawings; a sentence, say, will appear as a line of foliage on the horizon, or as the crest of a wave about to tumble upon the shore.

The letter I received in April was a lengthy note, signed by a body announcing itself as 'the Committee for the International Exhibition of Manufactures, 2051'. This was not an event of which I had been previously aware, though looking back I should perhaps have suspected that people of modernist persuasion would try to use the bicentenary of London's Great Exhibition of 1851 to try to prove their point: that industrial civilisation is on the point of returning.

'Dear Professor', began this communication, 'we are proud to announce that the City of London will this summer play host to the finest display of industrial manufactures for an entire generation. In this grand celebration of the industrial system it will become immediately obvious that the present recession is very nearly through. We welcome the world to see for itself the new confidence and the new optimism, and to witness the evidence that we will soon enjoy the service of machines once more. . . .'

Had it continued in that manner I would have cast it upon the fire at once: predictions regarding the end of the 'recession' have

worn thin over the past three decades. But being a vain man –
vanity, I am afraid, is a quality much associated with the elderly
these days – my attention was grabbed by the invitation which
followed:

'There can be no doubt, Professor, of your eminence in the
field of the history of the industrial age. The organising committee
would be truly honoured if you would care to grace the
exhibition by giving a public lecture. The subject could be of your
own choice, though you might consider making a presentation on
how in spite of current difficulties we look forward to a revival of
technology and international trade as a means of eradicating
poverty and promoting friendship and understanding amongst the
world's many peoples.'

I thought over the invitation for some time. There was much to
be said for it: it would provide me with an opportunity to lecture
to a sizeable audience on the nature of industrial society, and to
put right many of the misconceptions that have arisen. On the
negative side was the suspicion that this was an event being run by
dreamers. There are plenty of these about: we still have one or
two such people in Cambridge who dress up in business suits and
keep checking their non-functioning wrist-watches to see
whether it is time to head off for another imaginary appointment
or airline flight.

I do not mean to speak unkindly of such people; on the
contrary, I have considerable sympathy with them, having myself
grown up with the comforts of an industrialised society. In the end
I accepted the invitation more out of a sense of nostalgia than out
of a genuine belief that the industrial system could be revived. The
conferences, symposiums of our youth, where we used to go
around with name-badges, drink coffee from little plastic cups and
spend the afternoon slumbering while a technocrat at the podium
talked his way through graphs and flow charts: they may seem
mundane to you, but I assure you, once you have become familiar
with the world you now inhabit, you will think longingly of them.

Accepting the invitation to the exhibition posed a number of problems. Foremost was the question of how I was to reach London. To travel even modest distances these days is an adventure; travellers no longer take it for granted that they will survive their journeys. In Cambridge it is not uncommon to see people sitting by the roadside making the sign of the cross, so thankful are they that a brief walk from one of the surrounding villages had not ended with a cut throat or submergence in some swollen Fenland stream.

It is not all bad: the industrial age has bequeathed us some fine stretches of road, and at least one credible means of swift travel: the skateboard. Having no moving parts other than their wheels, skateboards are tolerated by the Progressives where cars and motorcycles are not. Even bicycles are frowned upon by the Progressive committees which have been set up to decide which products of the industrial age are acceptable and which are not. Most forms of transportation are outlawed by virtue of their possessing chains and shafts: signs of evil mechanisation. But the skateboard? Few Progressives can establish a case for prohibiting these, so long as the skater does not attempt to travel long distances. The people of Cambridge buzz backwards and forwards all day, the older folk in particular being quite proficient at flicking their boards over kerbs and sundry obstructions, having retained these skills from their youth. It may seem odd to you, who no doubt remember skateboarding as a juvenile hobby, but injuries apart it serves us well.

Or at least it does so long as we remain within the confines of villages and towns. Venture beyond, and you are into bandit country. Wise travellers avoid the old motorways in particular: those roads have become great wooded canyons where robbers hang about waiting to snare any poor skateboarder foolish enough to be tempted by the narrowed ribbons of tarmac left between the encroaching undergrowth. The byways are safer, though they do have a tendency, after miles of easy progress, to deliver you to the banks of impassable streams, the bridges which once crossed them having been washed away. It is the loss of bridges and sluices which have made the environs of Cambridge a particularly difficult place in which to travel: landscapes which in your day were considered tame have become impenetrable wastes. The clay lowlands have tended to become more backward and less populated than the uplands, where there is less surface water and it is easier to get about.

For most people there is an additional disincentive to travel: it is frowned upon by their masters. Travel is now synonymous with disease. This is not wholly unreasonable, for many of the diseases which afflict us nowadays almost certainly originated in the tropics and were brought here courtesy of aeroplanes in the industrial age. You remember that old saying 'the Global Village'? Sorry to say that it is remembered not as a happy community where people would chat to each other across continents as they would across the village green. It is remembered as a plague village. Fears of disease are exaggerated beyond all proportion. It is widely believed nowadays that a human body which has been in transit for more than a couple of dozen miles begins to decay to the point at which infection by mortal disease or death by interruption of the blood supply becomes inevitable. Towns will frequently refuse to admit travellers altogether or else insist upon their first being ducked into the river to 'cleanse' them. Travellers often catch a chill from their cleansing': which for the Progressives merely reinforces the theory that travellers are the carriers of mortal disease.

Once I had accepted the dangers of travelling to London I began to assemble a party to accompany me. The majority of my party, naturally, would be made up of my scholars, though I considered it necessary to recruit some younger and fitter people too. Most of us at Trinity were of advanced age, it no longer being easy to recruit younger people for a life of scholarship. Even those few who are attracted to study find the life difficult; the main problem is that younger people are so overwhelmed by the weight of documents left over from the industrial age that they find it hard to distinguish between what is and what is not important. I have seen them many a time poring over old junk mail catalogues, convincing themselves that within them must lay some important detail about the lost civilisation. They think they must read everything, and so merely end up with a headache.

My first approach was to Dr Anders Hoeffel, an elderly human rights lawyer. His field of study was enough to make him something of a pariah in the current age. You will be lucky to hear or see a lawyer these days, save for the straw dummies dressed in white wigs and pinstripe suits which are dragged around market squares and burned on bonfires on 5 November: a day which has come to mark the demise of the legal system of the industrial age. Dr Hoeffel lived in fear that he too would one day be treated like the dummies. As a result, we had made for him a hiding-hole behind one of the fireplaces in the Master's Lodge, stocked with sufficient provisions to last him a week. For him, London represented a flight to relative safety: 'To get to London will be a feat, but I have heard it is safer there,' he told me. 'It is said that people remain more internationalist in their outlook there, and that there are several cells of human rights lawyers still operating.'

You must understand that the concept of sorting out disagreements in a courtroom without a blow being struck is foreign to most people today; brute force has re-emerged as the most common way of settling disputes. At the end of the industrial age the masses came to resent the power that became vested in the legal profession. They came to despise its arcane language and the personal wealth which lawyers were amassing. The legal profession came to be seen as a conspiracy of the mentally agile against the physically strong; and the strong fought back. At this point, lawyers were dragged from their chambers and their fast cars, beaten and left for dead. Courthouses were destroyed. The police forces, who themselves had long been at odds with the courts, changed sides and joined the rule of the mob.

I do not mean to alarm you unduly: we are not wholly barbarians, not yet. In reality, disputes rarely result in death; more usually, threat and injury are enough to settle them. Various professionals – bailiffs, debt collectors and a shady body of men known as 'arbitrators' or 'mediators' – have taken over where the lawyers left off. Oddly, a smattering of legal language has survived the demise of lawyers, to be used euphemistically in the written threats which fly backwards and forwards between lord and servant, tradesman and customer. 'Pay your debts by six 'o clock on Tuesday or you will be sentenced,' might serve as a warning to expect a visit from a man armed with an iron railing. Wrongdoers are still occasionally condemned by things called juries, though these invariably consist of a few accomplices hurriedly assembled by the Lord of the Manor or the Chairman of the Parish Council. Most peculiarly of all, the expression 'human rights' is still flung about, though in an ironic context. 'Don't you dare start taking human rights with me,' is one commonly-used expression.

After Dr Hoeffel I called upon Alferris, our Welsh-born Dean of Chapel. A middle-aged man of solid build and bushy sideburns, he was just about old enough still to remember the industrial age; for him, to attend the exhibition would be to rediscover a lost childhood. Besides, it would have been unthinkable to have left for London without a priest. Men of holy orders are treated with great reverence. You will remember that when you fell asleep, God had either ceased to exist or had come to be seen as such a friendly fellow that few saw the need to acknowledge His existence, let alone give their time to prayer? Well, God is back and is more fearsome than ever. Few dare go to their graves without first making peace with Him. As a result, Alferris was able to earn the college a living by being constantly on call to offer prayers for the dying and to conduct committals for the dead.

It is remarkable that such a strong revival of religion should have followed a largely secular age. Yet economic collapse has done wonders for religious belief. The churches and chapels are overflowing. Some have had to be re-consecrated after having spent the latter part of the industrial age as shops, homes, restaurants and what have you. Some churches are entirely new; I know of one erstwhile fast food restaurant which has recently been converted into a church. Services are solemn, though they have incorporated hymns whose tunes, and some of whose words, you will recognise as pop music. It must come as a great oddity to you to learn that when people sing the word 'Babe' they mean 'Lord'.

Prayers are very different to those being said fifty years ago. For you, the words must sound strange; they have adopted some of the language of the insurance industry. 'Dear Lord, we have reason to make claim upon our policy with you,' begins one popular prayer. Another contains the words 'Forgive us, oh Lord, our accidental damage, for which we admit fault'. It is no coincidence that church attendance received its biggest boost in the months which followed the collapse of the insurance market. Religion has expanded to replace the sense of financial security which people lost at the end of the industrial age.

There is some pleasure in seeing the churches full, especially for those of us who remember them empty. But the revival of religion is not altogether a pleasant thing. Alferris was in the liberal tradition, yet far more priests these days are fundamentalist in their outlook. They take the Old Testament at its word and view the science of the industrial era as a dangerous heresy. Even to speak of evolution or the big bang is sure to draw violent protest from the church – a tragedy in Cambridge, which once prided itself in its work in those fields. At Trinity, we had books on evolution and astrophysics hidden away in the college, in preparation, so we hoped, of a revival in scientific learning at some point in the future. But most other works have by now been seized and burned in public. And it is not just books. It distresses me to say that one of my scholars, a physicist who was engaged in work on black holes, was accosted while walking in a fundamentalist part of Cambridge and, after a bitter argument in one of the taverns, was, we believe, tied to a wooden post near Jesus College and set alight. These incidents are rare, but it is a sorry thing that they happen at all.

Alferris was soon won over by my invitation to the exhibition. The sponsors, I told him, were promising motor-cars, computers and televisions. The exhibition hall, I added, was rumoured to be centrally-heated, and the organisers were even promising to put on a railway service from Stevenage all the way to London. 'Then I shall come,' he said. 'It is years since I last saw Royston, let alone London. I do not share the distaste for travel which has taken root in this city: I shall be pleased to take my mission elsewhere.'

Yet I knew these tales of riches were likely to have been exaggerated, for although I had not been to London for many years I knew full well that since the end of the industrial age the metropolis had acquired a reputation for being far poorer than the country which surrounds it. But as you will soon realize, this is an age of tall tales. The objectivity so treasured by industrial folk has passed out of fashion. People like and expect their news to be embellished with myth; they want their history to be dressed up with fiction. You will be surprised to hear what they make of the industrial age. After Alferris, I approached a workman in his 20s, Edgar, whom we used to employ around college. Might he be interested in joining our party?

'An exhibition of industrial goods?' he asked, visibly shaking. 'I don't want nothing to do with machines. If we go to London they will get us!' I protested that machines were inanimate, but he would have none of it. 'But they were terrible creatures, motor-cars. My mother tells me of when she was a girl and she was told under pain of death to keep away from them: "Don't go up to the main road," she used to say, "or the traffic will get you." Sometimes children would go up to the main road, and they

never came back. I know some people say they don't believe in
the evil of cars, saying they were just dumb things and it was really
the drivers that were to blame. But people weren't people any
more when they were behind a driving wheel, were they? They
were under the control of the machines. You've just got to look
in the eyes of those old cars, haven't you. I can't go past the
scrapheap on Newmarket Road without feeling the horror of it
all. There's a dead one up there with a great smirk on its face. I'm
sure as can be that it was the one which killed my grandfather.'

2

Now that you are beginning to stretch those aching limbs of yours there is one thing you must fear more than any other. You surely twinged when I mentioned the plague: having survived against the odds, it would be unfortunate if you were to be carried off again so quickly. Yours is a genuine concern: though infectious disease has failed to eradicate us, it has had a run of good seasons. The sudden cough of a passer-by in the street, which half a century ago seemed the most trivial of events, is now a grave matter. Heads will turn, comments will be muttered; the one who coughed will be avoided and the coughed-over will turn away, to spend the rest of the day worrying that every tickle in the throat is the beginning of an untreatable illness.

People speak of the plague, though the disease that we call the plague is not what ancient history knew as the plague. In fact, it might not be a single disease at all. It is characterised by a swelling of the neck, which may be indicative of deficiencies of minerals in the diet. Weakened by their condition, sufferers become subject to fevers and vomiting, leading to delirium and death. It is not unknown these days for whole villages to be abandoned due to outbreaks of the disease.

But the mortal aspect of the present age ought not to be

exaggerated. There seems to be an accommodation between us and microbiotic disease which ensures that neither gets the upper hand for long. While common ailments may more quickly progress towards death than they did in your day, there is protection against their wider spread in that we live in smaller units and travel much less. It is common to find villages decimated by disease, while just over the hill people are still healthy, unaware even of what is happening. Not all bugs in any case have taken advantage of the decline of medical science. Some of the most malignant diseases of the late industrial age have failed to realize their threat. It is not uncommon to hear people in the streets, discussing the health of a relative, saying 'by Godly grace, the illness is not grave. It is just a touch of Aids.' That particular illness has mysteriously mellowed and now means nothing worse than the odd day or two in bed. Nobody knows why, because molecular biology is no longer practised, though most take a religious view: that Aids was a punishment – for an excessive consumption of medicine, according to the popular theory at present – and that because mankind is now so thoroughly punished, and has begun to reform, God has withdrawn the virus from service. Perhaps it would be closer to the truth to say that the virus has acquired wisdom, and has come to realize that it is not in its interests to kill its host.

We were fortunate at Trinity College to have a physician, Dr Olga Khan, who would be invaluable on our journey. Though she could not offer surgery – to open up the human body is these days a guaranteed way of ensuring a swift death by infection, and is now considered a heresy – she did have in her possession some medical drugs which she had retained since the industrial age. She had to be careful: her cough mixtures and antibiotic pills had to be kept from view. Possession of anything recognisable as a medicine can earn you persecution from the Progressives. Substances with scientific names are commonly seized and their owners imprisoned – or 'admitted for detoxification' as the progressives like to euphemise.

Doctors and medicines of the industrial age are blamed for all ills. The drug addicts of half a century ago are talked about to disbelieving children, the addicts' moods and fevers cited as damning evidence of the polluting effect of medicine upon the human body. In place of drugs have come herbal preparations: teas, ointments, dried mixtures which you smoke in a pipe. They are administered not by 'doctors' but by people whom are termed 'healers'. Any cure-all whose form is not too obviously removed from plant-life is considered wholesome, while anything which resembles the perfectly-rounded pills or homogeneous solutions of industrial medicine is considered evil. It leads to some inconsistencies: parents will tell their children tall stories of how back in the industrial age unsuspecting citizens were deliberately turned into zombies by state doctors who dripped heroin into their veins – while at the same time those parents will gather poppies from the roadside and grind them into tea to help their children into a listless sleep.

Olga was quickly won around to the idea of visiting London, not least because she reckoned it would remove us from the path of a virulent plague which had visited the village of Great Shelford, three miles upwind of our college. There, it was rumoured, a couple of hundred souls had been wiped out in the preceding weeks, from an epidemic which is typical of our times: it began slowly with a few deaths dotted about, then tore its way through the village. Then, at the point at which it seemed the entire population was doomed to die, mysteriously it fizzled out; and the bewildered, grieving survivors were left humbly thanking the Lord that they had been spared.

'I have long wished to visit the remaining medical schools in London,' said Olga. 'It is my wish to present to them a study on the enfeeblement of people today. I must take some measurements and write a paper.' It is hard to explain the ill-feeling that such a suggestion makes upon people today. Study is an activity alien to current thinking; study of the human body, especially, generates deep suspicion. Rather, people rely on intuition. Should they

encounter a black spot on their neck, they will quickly say something like 'I know it is a cancer caused by the pollution of the
industrial age', and onlookers will accept their diagnosis without
doubt. They will then pray for what they call 'compensation' – by
which they mean the wrong done to them will be put right in the
next life.

People carry around in their heads all kinds of medical terms
which have been passed down to them, but whose meaning has
been skewed. Some believe a tumour to be made up of negative
energy which the sufferer may be able to flush from the body by
experiencing feelings of shame over the harm wrought on the
planet by industrial age Man. A heart attack is imagined to be
caused by a microchip which has sprung from one of the millions
of broken appliances still lying around our towns and somehow
entered the body. It is a peculiar idea which seems to have
stemmed from pacemakers exploding in the chests of elderly
people as they are cremated – and undertakers and not knowing
what the devices were nor how they got there.

Besides the medical considerations, we had also to think of our
safety on our way to London. It was beyond doubt that we would
be attacked if we announced our intention to visit London. In the
surrounding countryside, the metropolis has become synonymous
with the corruption and brutality of the industrial age. Those who
venture there are invariably subject to suspicion. The banks and
commercial headquarters of London are seen as the bastions of an
enemy which has been 99 per cent defeated, but in which no-one
can be entirely sure there do not remain groups of stubborn
resistance fighters waiting to revive the evil machinery responsible
for human enfeeblement and environment degradation. The
image of a business lunch at some air-conditioned hotel in the late
industrial age is seen in the same light as a monstrously rich
banquet in the latter stages of the Roman Empire. The arrogance
and misplaced self-confidence of industrial age businessmen causes

much wonderment: could they not see, those besuited figures through their tinted windows, that history would engulf their society just as it had done imperialism before them? It doesn't matter how much one might protest that the industrial age was one of health and happiness. A society which valued people through the quantities of material goods they had managed to accumulate during their lives is now seen as a contemptible thing. The materialist who cherished his car and his swimming pool is regarded in the same light as the medieval churchman who held icons sacred. The 'false gods' of consumer goods are regularly smashed and burned in orgies of destruction, in which zealots set to work with flailing hammers and flaming torches dripping with duck fat. These events have been going on for years, and show no sign of subsiding, owing to the sheer quantity of manufactured goods left behind from the industrial age. The waste-disposal mechanisms which could dispose of junk quickly and effectively are no more, and so the remains of the offending articles remain strewn about the streets.

There is one exception to the general disregard for the leftovers of the industrial age: consumable items. Much though the Progressives warn against them, old tins of food are revered by the well-off. One evening my scholars and I had been invited to dine at the table of a local landowner, who had spared no effort in showing off to us his considerable wealth. He served us tainted beer from corroded aluminium cans and sardines from rusty tins. Tinned foods have become regarded as a great luxury because they are scarce and are therefore beyond the reach of the masses. The older the tin, the sillier the price. It is widely believed that canned fish improve with age. The fact that diners occasionally succumb to food poisoning from tinned foods merely adds to their mystique, and therefore their value.

We still possess and use money, though you will not recognise it. Any notes and coins that were left about your body when you were frozen will not buy you anything today. People have long since lost confidence in the currency which was in circulation when you suffered your accident: too much of it existed only in the form of electronic pulses whizzing between computers, and vanished with the machines themselves. Pre-industrial coins are widely accepted: generally, the older the coin the more it is considered to be worth, irrespective of its face value. Gold has re-emerged as a medium of exchange, though not every community has adopted it. Many other kinds of money have evolved: old stamps, bracelets, dog-eared copies of the Bible. In parts of Scotland, I am informed by scholars who have passed that way, the most accepted currency is the oatcake, with the 'calorie' the basic unit of exchange. The oatcakes are stamped with '50 calories' or '100 calories', with people boasting of the number of 'calories' they possess. In times of famine, many of the biscuits get eaten and the money supply collapses. Inevitably, the currency appreciates and prices fall. Those who benefit are those who hoard money; indeed great fortunes have been made by those who have stashed their 'calories' beneath their mattress.

It was an awkward business deciding what money we should take to London, it being necessary to carry currencies which would be of interest in every town that we might visit. To this end, we raided our college's collection of silver plate, along with various other treasures which scholars had managed to salvage from the Fitzwilliam Museum before that building was seized by the Progressives some years back. Ancient artefacts, no matter how obscure their origin, are universally prized. In most respects, the public is far more ignorant than it was half a century ago; people know little about the second world war and have a skewed knowledge of the industrial revolution. But it is remarkable how their ignorance ceases when it comes to identifying ancient swords and brooches. Even the poorest, roughest types who would never have ventured into a museum during the industrial age, have developed a keen eye for detail. Their eyes light up at the mention of terms like 'Hellenic' and 'Fourth Dynasty'. The

miller to whom you present a Roman marble will examine it with
the care of a scholar and comment upon its origin before deciding
whether it is worth one loaf of bread or two. It would be wrong
to interpret this as a genuine interest in culture, in the sense that
industrial folk used that word. But for scholars struggling to
maintain human knowledge through this dark age it is a sign of
hope.

3

My party was now ready to leave for London, but I had not reckoned with the obstacle that was now to be thrown in our way. The morning before we were due to leave I received a letter from our Lord of the Manor, Julius Holder, summoning me to see him at once. Holder being now the effective dictator of Cambridge, I had little option but to obey his summons.

He was to be found in his usual place, an upstairs room at his headquarters, the former Fitzwilliam Museum, which had been hung with spears and banners in an attempt to recreate the atmosphere of a medieval hall. At first sight it was impressive, but to older eyes there was something a little odd about this design: the banners were clearly upturned flags emblazoned with the corporate logo of a long-extinct manufacturer of motor cars. Holder had acquired the flags during his previous career as a motor-car salesman, when they had been hoisted outside his showroom. Though he had long since denounced motor-cars the logo had been adopted as his own personal emblem, and few people were aware of its true origins. In its heraldry and in many other aspects, too, the neo-feudalism which has engulfed the country is engrained with vestiges of industrialisation.

Seated upon a 'throne' at the far end of the room Holder was an imposing figure: though now in his mid 60s and with silver hair trailing over his shoulders, his eyes revealed a still-potent mind and an unforgiving temper. He had a substantial build, to which I suspect he owed much of his power: bulk counts for much now that a leader's stature can no longer be magnified via the medium of the television screen. In contrast to the 20th century democrat, who earned virtue points by being photographed jogging around the park, Holder, it was proudly put about, spent long hours at the dining table deliberately in order to increase his size.

Holder's many layers of clothing were topped by a loosely-knitted smock, while upon his head was a baseball-style cap fashioned from cat-fur — a much-favoured material these days thanks to the abundance of cats running wild in our towns. For all the baronial pretensions of his hall, Holder's general appearance was ragged; the art of tailoring was lost during the age of machine-stitching, and ancient skills such as these are only slowly being regained. There is little incentive to buy new clothes when there is still a vast stock of twentieth century garments available at low prices from old shops and warehouses. It takes a progressive zealot like Julius Holder to want to have his clothes made for him.

Holder gestured for me to hasten my journey through his hall, and I obliged.

'Professor Gonne,' he said. 'I have heard rumours that you are proposing to visit the metropolis. Do wish to confirm them or deny them?'

'It is not my business to lie, your lordship,' I said. 'I am indeed planning an excursion to London.'

'And I understand that the purpose of your visit is to take part in an event being dubbed "the International Exhibition of Industrial Manufactures?"'

'That is correct.'

'It sounds a very decadent event to me, Professor. What is it that attracts you to make this futile journey into the past?'

'It would be an insult to my scholarship if I did not attend.'

'But you are aware of the dangers, I presume: that by encouraging an interest in machinery you are tempting people back into the physical laziness that so afflicted mankind during the industrial age. You will be guilty of trying to break down the order and peace which has become established in England since the end of that era.' He paused, and looked me up and down. 'Perhaps these matters are of no concern to you, Professor, as you are an old man and have not long for this world. But it would certainly be in your interest to know the conditions which exist in the metropolis at the moment. There is an epidemic of typhoid fever, for which can be blamed the city's continuing habit of welcoming foreign ships. Outsiders have reduced the city to chaos. It is ridden with thieves, prostitutes and murderers who would quite happily kill you for a few crumbs. I do hope for your sake, professor, that you know who is running this exhibition of yours, for they are quite likely to be criminals themselves.'

'Would it satisfy you to know, your Lordship, that the King has leant the enterprise his support?'

Holder frowned. The King presented him with something of a problem. As a Lord of the Manor Holder theoretically owed his allegiance to the King. The trouble was that the King, like you and me, is a child of the industrial age. He does not wish to preside over a hierarchy of provincial barons; instead he clings, pathetically, to the few remaining threads of liberalism and democracy. He still resides at Buckingham Palace where he entertains the odd foreign dignitary. Every year he traipses over to Westminster in order to open his now meaningless parliament. And still he engages in the ancient tradition of addressing his people at Christmas time, as if he believes there are still television cameras broadcasting his words unto the nation. He was considered by Holder to be a dangerous reactionary.

'He is the king of another century,' said Holder. 'I do not think we need to take his views seriously. He is tainted with the worst excesses of the industrial age: you cannot be ignorant, surely, of the reputation which royalty acquired during the latter years of the industrial era: the irresponsibility, the high living, the debts. And in any case, I do not consider that we are a kingdom any longer: the King has been usurped by a revolution from the very grassroots: the lords of the manors. It is obvious that mankind is better administered in small units of population. That is the way things will be done in the future. The King may look after his patch, the ruined city of London, and I will look after mine.'

Holder paused while one servant arrived to shave him and another presented him with a pewter platter topped with a small mound of snuff. He was not alone in this habit: smoking is now widely believed to be a means by which industrialists attempted to kill off the masses, but snuff is another matter: to take it is considered a sign of wealth and importance. Holder had no doubt already been shaven once that morning. I had the feeling that this was a little show put on for my benefit: it is the use of servants rather than the accumulation of possessions that has become the yardstick by which the wealthy judge their success. The houses of the rich swarm with maids and butlers, attending to little tasks that were once trusted to electrical appliances. Industrial age Man, on the other hand, is pitied for his having to live with the noise and vibrations of domestic machines.

I went on: 'I am not entirely certain why you have brought me here. My only purpose in visiting London is the innocent study of the industrial era. I seek only to explain why people like yourself, who as a motor-car salesman was in the thick of industrialisation, should now be so heavily against the age in which you were born.'

Holder glowered at me, for he did not like to be reminded that he had once been in the motor trade. 'I think you are intelligent enough to realize, Professor, that it was necessary to fight for revolution from within. I entered the motor-car trade because it was expected of me: my father and grandfather had been in the car business. But I am proud of having played a part in the revolution, and mankind has progressed to a point at which such an occupation is obsolete.'

'I am afraid I do not share your view of events, your lordship. Rather I think of you as an opportunist. You were a motor-car dealer because you believed that was the way you could most easily make yourself rich, and when the industrial age came to an end you became a feudalist because you realized that was the way to advance your standing in society. You would follow in whichever way the wind was blowing. I cannot blame you for that, for opportunism is what has kept mankind on his feet, but I do wish that men like yourself would stop trying to make an ideology out of the miserable state in which mankind now finds himself living.'

'Professor, it is a shock and a disappointment to learn that there are people who still think like you do in this day and age. I defy you to say that you were not appalled by the conditions in which Englishmen had to live half a century ago. It was beneath human dignity the way in which people were forcibly divorced from husbandry, had no direct contact with the ploughing, reaping and gleaning which sustains human civilisation, and instead had to go and work in offices which offered neither daylight nor fresh air. Consider the way in which people were frequently left without any means of employment whatsoever: to deprive people of their sense of purpose and belonging is a cruelty which would not be tolerated in these more enlightened times. Thankfully, we have moved on since the end of the industrial era, and men no longer have any doubt as to where and to whom they belong.'

On this last point Holder was not exaggerating: he was referring to a new brand of feudalism which he had helped to pioneer. It is, in effect, slavery, but rebranded with some of the terminology of the industrial era. In Cambridge, in common with much of rural England these days, men can choose either to be free, or, for a depressingly small sum, opt to become a 'stakeholder' for their lord. Such people are assured of being fed, clothed and generally looked after, but in return have to work for their lord for a hundred days a year or more. In addition, they have to ask their lord permission should they wish to make any changes to their situation, such as marrying, or to undertake any alterations to their person, such as growing a beard. Once they have committed themselves to it there is very little likelihood of these people being able to buy their way out of stakeholdership and become 'freeholders'. It is a demeaning business, becoming a stakeholder, but I am afraid it is a route which too many Englishmen have been tempted to take, so desperate has the situation of many former professional workers become.

'Professor,' continued Holder. 'I do not wish to prolong this meeting, for I have other important business to attend to. You are perfectly aware that I cannot stop you travelling to London, because you are not a stakeholder. All I can do is to offer you kindly advice, in order that you might protect your life and also your estimable reputation as a scholar. I can tell from your responses that you are in no mood to follow that advice, and so I can do nothing further for you other than to pray for you. You are dismissed.'

I turned and went, omitting the customary bow. How I despised the man and how determined I was to flee to London, where the great majority of men are still free, in spite of the problems of surviving in that place. Nevertheless, our meeting had left me feeling tense; for I could not quite be confident that Holder would not attempt to prevent us from travelling. It was not clear how much power and influence Holder had beyond the confines of the city.

I walked back down to the Market Square, where a fine rain was falling. The air was sultry and made me cough. Cambridge, like all towns these days, is pervaded by an ever-present tang of burnt plastics; in the absence of coal and sufficient firewood people burn anything which lies to hand. This includes old furniture, much of which was upholstered with synthetic fibres and fills the air with large quantities of black, oily smoke. As a result, the air in towns and villages tends to be more polluted than it was at the height of the industrial era. Not that people believe this: most maintain that the foul air in towns today is left over from the industrial age when, they have convinced themselves, men could hardly breathe at all. 'Look,' one young student told me one day, 'this is how people of the industrial age had to breathe'. And he handed me a photograph of a diver on a dockside, wearing an oxygen mask.

The fussy air of the Market Square was made even more nauseating by a commotion in the far corner. A crowd had gathered amidst a swirl of smoke and the shrill screams of a human in pain. It did not take long to work out what was going on: an unfortunate bystander had been singed by a sheet of flame which had seared up through the old drains. This is by no means an unusual experience in towns nowadays: the drainage systems of the industrial age have long since stagnated, leaving a huge mass of vegetable matter mouldering below the streets. Over time this has built up a huge head of foul gas, which is relieved by the odd spontaneous explosion.

On this occasion, thankfully, the fire had been quickly contained. But spontaneous fires are commonplace: there are burned-out buildings on every corner of Cambridge. Other buildings have collapsed as the drains have given way beneath their foundations. With an abundance of houses left over from the industrial era, it makes no sense to rebuild any that become damaged; the occupants simply abandon them and move further down the street. To buy or rent a property costs next to nothing, and to maintain it makes little financial sense.

Everyone speaks of the appalling legacy which their forefathers have left behind. People of my own generation, who were young adults during the last years of the industrial age, are almost universally treated with contempt. 'Why did you hate your grandchildren so much?' is a question frequently asked of us. To escape the condemnation of younger people it is necessary, as Julius Holder and other Progressives have done, to persuade people that you spent the last years of the industrial age engaged in revolution against it. In most cases this is stretching the truth. It is true that a revolutionary movement grew out of the environmentalist pressure groups of the turn of the century, and that this movement was able to hinder industrial progress. But this is far from the whole story: the truth is that Julius Holder and his like only joined the 'revolution' out of expedience when industrial civilisation was on its knees. Progressives have only emerged as a force in the past few years.

The anti-industrialist fervour has now reached such proportions that all machinery has come to be seen as the work of the devil himself. In parts of rural England it has become a crime to be seen attempting to restore a machine or to use any substance resembling a man-made chemical. The last man to attempt to ride a moped in Cambridge, half a dozen years ago, came to a violent end. The unfortunate victim was forced to sit upon his machine and to rev up its engine; meanwhile a noose was placed around his neck and the clutch let out so that he was quickly strangled, to the accompaniment of great cheering. The moped, with his decomposing body still upon it, was hoisted upon the railings outside the old Senate House and left there for many months.

Earlier this summer, the attitudes of the Progressives were hardening fast. They stirred much fervour by inventing a mythology of the revolution which had supposedly freed the world from industrialisation. Holder was one of the worst offenders. In the afternoon following our encounter, he was to be found high on a podium in Cambridge Market Square, standing before a statue which was covered with sacking. Removing the sacking, he then delivered a speech to two or three hundred onlookers:

'Hail a woman of vision, who was persecuted for what she knew to be right. Henceforth, may her memory come to bear upon our city, and her example inspire us in all we do. This woman lived half a century ago, yet she was ahead of her time, and her struggles were viewed with fear and incomprehension. But now, in these more enlightened times, we can honour her as the true seer of the revolution that she was. I am proud to present to you, beneath this cloak, the form of Nell Ludd.'

And to much cheering the sheet was pulled away to reveal a stooped female figure in a short duffle coat and armed with a brick, the whole lot coarsely chiselled out of a tree trunk. Red-chested labourers who had shinned their way up old lamp-posts to gain themselves a better view of this monstrosity waved their fists in the air. Dirt-encrusted boys who knew nothing of the industrial age cheered for the hell of it. A lady rushed forwards to lay flowers at the foot of the statue, and at the fringes of the crowd a drunkard took an enormous celebratory gulp of fermented sugar beet – the sickly spirit which has become the lifeblood of East Anglia's labourers.

It was no use trying to tell these people that Nell Ludd never existed. The popular historians of the present day do not wish to be bridled by fact. Several storytellers do the rounds of Cambridge taverns reading the story of Nell, shamelessly inventing the history of a woman who never was. Nell Ludd is the King Arthur of our times: one version of her tale places her as an environmental activist who succeeded in shutting down a nuclear power station in Cumbria. Another has her as a native of East Anglia, who cut down the fields of genetically-modified crops and banished them from our shores. Dozens of towns claim a connection, one of the most fanciful of them describing her as Queen of the Lud-ites – a race of giants who once inhabited the city of Ludlow and fought and won a brave battle of resistance against an evil band of men, known as the Supermarketeers, who wanted to lay waste to the city.

'I want you all to learn the story of Nell Ludd and the resistance movement which she led,' Holder went on. 'And then to ask yourselves, in all honesty, what would I have done if had been born in her shoes, and what will I do should the need ever arise again to stamp upon the evils of globalisation? Would you have stood by and done nothing, as so many people did, only to be driven to their deaths in trains and motor-cars or else killed by cancers and heart attacks? Or would you have stood up and fought? What would have been your choice?'

My role in resisting the Progressives has itself hardly been glorious; I am sorry to say that I have too often capitulated to them for fear of my own safety. But I nevertheless was on this occasion so outraged by Holder's reinvention of himself that I heard myself shouting out: 'Your choice was to go into the motor trade which you now claim to despise!'

There was a collective gasp in the crowd around me. There were cries of 'seize that man!'. But I was fortunate in that my words had not carried to Holder himself. The crowd returned to a hush, and I even discovered that I had one or two sympathisers amongst the crowd. A blotchy lady on my right hand side held her breath, then said, with a damp, drooling smile:

'Ooh, you old-fashioned cynic. I do love to hear your sort. There's so few people around these days who are prepared to have a dig at authority, aren't there? They're all believers, now. That's what the trouble is.'

She came closer, and whispered into my ear: 'Don't you just want to wring their necks, these Progressives? They've no sense of heritage whatsoever. I know we all had to work much longer hours in those days and there was so much rushing around just to keep your house and home together, but in some ways things were so much better, weren't they? People were so much brighter when they had the television to watch. Now they just sit staring at the wall.'

I wished the woman a good day and turned to leave, but she grabbed my arm and pulled me back with a jolt. It was not meant rudely: having become a cruder, more tactile people, we no longer carry with us our invisible envelopes of space and it is considered quite acceptable to accost people in this way nowadays.

'Oi, can I ask you just one thing,' she went on. 'Are you Professor Gonne, the Master of Trinity?'

I acknowledged that I was.

'I've been trying to find you for days, sir. Is it true, this rumour that you are planning an excursion to London, to see all the sights? You know, the underground railway stations, the underpasses, the tower blocks and all that?'

'That is true, but I would appreciate it if you would just lower your voice, for it is a very controversial issue.'

'That doesn't make any difference to me, Prof. I still want to go, and I want my son to go too.' She then introduced me to a sickly-looking youth, whose name she said was 'Bump': quite typical of the uncomplicated names which have become popular these days. 'Any chance we could join you, professor?'

'The journey has its risks, you have to understand,' I said.

'We're prepared to put up with almost anything, just to catch a glimpse of how things used to be. I'm such a sucker for the olden days. But my Bump, you know, is getting mixed up with these Progressives. He keeps going off to folk dances, and he comes back with right funny ideas in his head that we old people were brought up in an immoral age. He won't even wear these fine old anoraks and trainers I buy him. Says he wants to be a weaver. He won't hear of it when I tell him how much fun life used to be. He says we were idiots because we couldn't comprehend the damage we were doing to the Earth. Every time there's a thunderstorm he says it's our punishment: he insists that lightning is made up of all the electricity of the industrial age reflected back on us. I tell him that's nonsense, but then he says I don't know any better because people in the old days were reduced to being zombies by the electricity and the chemicals. Very funny ideas, if you ask me. I want him to go to London so he can see for himself how far we've all come down in the world. Any chance, prof, that you could spare us a place on your trip?'

I turned to Bump and looked into his angry eyes and demanded of him: 'What is your ambition?'

Bump took his time to answer, then said through tight lips: 'Smash every machine in the country.'

'And what would be the purpose of that? There are very few left functioning.'

'I won't be satisfied until they are all gone.'

'It is very sad to hear you speak in this way. But you are hardly alone in these views: they are commonplace among the young. I shall look forward to you trying to convince me of your ideology. You and your mother will be welcome to join my party.'

I had intended to take no more people with me to London, but upon returning to college I discovered that my fellows had taken in a visitor. He was a travelling scholar from Spain by the name of Abdul. His name will require some explanation. During the dying years of industrial civilisation, Christians on the southern fringes of Europe, whose own churches had become weak, were over-run by the influence of Islam. When it came to providing leadership in difficult times, Christian churches had the disadvantage of being too closely identified with globalisation and industrialisation. Islam, on the other hand, was seen to represent earlier, less complicated and more moral civilisation. Thus it picked up easy souls when people began to turn against industrialisation. Moreover, muslims bred and multiplied healthily, while christians seemed to lose much of the urge to do so. Countries which abutted Islam fell in quick succession. The laws, the clothes, the names: all changed in a matter of a few years. Most of Spain is now muslim, along with the southern coast of France, and most of the Balkans. Islam has a strong base, too, in much of London, and in the former industrial cities of the north. It was to these places which Abdul had been heading.

What Abdul had to say surprised us much. In the late industrial age the Islamic world had come to be seen an austere place where people lived in fear of their religious leaders, but Abdul quickly won us over with his enthusiasm for his homeland. Terrible things had happened during his parents' day, twenty years before, he told us, but the people had won freedoms since then. The influence of religious leaders was strong, but was no longer absolute. 'The universities are becoming liberated,' he told us. 'A man at his books no longer has to look over his shoulder. There is no longer any restriction on what we can study. Not in Madrid, at any rate; though there is less of an understanding towards scholars in Barcelona, I hear.'

'What, you may even study the evolution of man?' I asked.

'I have read widely on the subject,' said Abdul.

'And astrophysics? And medicine?'

'But of course,' said Abdul.

'Then you are fortunate indeed. A long shadow has fallen over scholarship in the north of Europe. Do you know that we may not even study engineering any longer, because our priests believe that buildings are held up by the grace of God alone and it is not our business to intervene in His decision as to whether a building stands up or falls down? One of our own fellows ventured up to Ely to investigate a structural problem with the cathedral there, but when he got out his drawings and a tape measure he was driven away by a mob accusing him of interfering with God's work. People do not trust engineers because so many industrial age buildings have collapsed through neglect. They think that engineers built these structures deliberately in order to entomb innocent victims.'

Abdul laughed with disbelief. 'Many of my grandparents' generation had a suspicion against scientific learning, but this attitude is not widespread now. Some of the older people still frown at our study of industrial civilisation, but we do not allow their narrow-mindedness to affect us. Engineering is an art that we are following with great interest. In some quarters of Madrid, new buildings are going up, using debris from the old. The new buildings are not on the scale of the old ones, of course, but we see the new building as superior to the glasshouses of the industrial age. The old buildings become so hot in the summer that we cannot work out how people used to survive in them; we can only conclude that they were deliberately designed to make people sweat, to make them work harder. They are most intriguing.'

'But you must find our country so drab compared with your own, with so many marvellous things going on,' said Alferris.

'It has been a surprise to me how poor you are in the north,' said Abdul. 'At home, our markets are overflowing. Stalls are piled high with luxuries such as milk and flesh; and, to the disapproval of some of the older people, it is also possible to find wine for sale. Parts of Spain are being cultivated which have never been cultivated before.'

'Then what makes you want to come to such an impoverished island?' I asked.

'It is a visit undertaken by all students of industrial civilisation, to come to Britain,' he said. 'Many ancient sites of interest to us are in your country. You were the seat of industrialisation, and we admire your old civilisation in many ways; even though we laugh at its limitations. I intend to visit the Ironbridge Gorge, and the Stockton to Darlington railway. I have already been to the Cowley motor factory, which is of great interest to us.'

'That is a strange choice,' I said. 'It was never considered a place of great beauty.'

'That you did not care for it is obvious from my visit. I cannot understand why you allow it to fall into such decay. Can you believe this: that much of the asbestos has been torn down by the people of Oxford to use for makeshift repairs to their roofs? And there is no-one who seems to be concerned at the practice! The machine tools inside the factory: they are being left to rust. It is so sad that you do not have pride in these things. I am considering collecting some of these treasures for which you do not care, and having them shipped back to Madrid.

'The history of Industrialisation has become a very popular

subject of study at our universities. The romance of it is irresistible. Barely 50 years ago the Industrial Empire stretched most of the way around the world. Though it was resisted in the muslim world, we were enthralled by its power and its presence. It seemed there was nothing which could stop your empire, certainly not the terrorists who blew themselves up in your cities at the beginning of the religious wars; theirs was a futile gesture. And yet your civilisation then decayed so rapidly and so totally that there is nothing left of it but the relicts. We liken your old culture to the bear and ours to the rabbit: yours so impressive and strong, ours so feeble and nervous. And yet it was yours which succumbed to falling numbers, ours which had the fecundity to prevail. You possessed the military and economic strength; but it was us who won the only battle which mattered in the longer run: the demographic one.

'It is remarkable how your civilisation rotted from within, how you lost the will to create, how you lost the will to breed, how you allowed yourselves to be corrupted by hedonistic pleasures. Your cities, they became over-run with drunken and drug-crazed people; how were they expected to maintain the health of your civilizations? But above all we look with astonishment upon how the brave spirit of your civilization became suppressed beneath a welter of apology. When you read the writings of the late industrial age, there is this one theme which comes through: you seemed to think that you were harming the Earth, poisoning the air, starving and drowning the poor in other parts of the world. Whatever it was that went wrong in the world, whether it be war, famine, disease or natural disaster, your writers seemed always to seek blame from within. How miserable it must have been to bear these responsibilities! No wonder you destroyed your civilization so spectacularly. We have come to the conclusion that you evolved a collective wish to commit suicide while suffering from delusions of self-imposed guilt.'

That Abdul would want to come to London with us went

without saying. He had not heard of the exhibition of industrial manufactures, but listened with great excitement. We would leave, we told him, at first light. But first we wanted to show him around our college. We began with the Great Court which, though it has lost some of its elegance, now performs a vital role as the college's kitchen garden. The turf has been replaced with vegetables, around which pigs and chickens roam freely. Most of the time, we told him, we ate well, though sometimes our elder fellows lamented the passing of convenience food. They complained that the food did not have the colour which it used to, and that it turned them flatulent. Abdul was surprised by our husbandry, saying that he did not believe it to be the work of scholars to feed themselves: did we not have staff? Regretfully, we told him that scholarship did not pay its way and that it was necessary to support ourselves. We had to tend our garden every afternoon even if it meant there was only the morning left for study.

We then took Abdul to our library, where we showed him our works on history and the arts. After exchanging a few secret words with Olga, however, I decided to terminate the visit before we reached the scientific works. Though we believed Abdul to be a genuine scholar, you cannot quite tell these days; there was the fear that me might just possibly be a spy in the pay of the Progressives.

Before we retired to our beds – something which we, in common with most people these days, tend to do soon after sundown – Alferris had the idea of inviting Abdul to evensong at the cathedral; the church formerly known as Great St Mary's. Inside the west door, we stooped to light a candle, and handed one to Abdul. 'What is this for?' he whispered. 'It is expected of us,' said Alferris. 'It happens in all our churches these days. It is supposed to be in memory of all the unborn babies who were terminated during the industrial age.'

'The babies who were terminated?'

'The practice known as abortion, or the Holocaust as it has come to be called.'

'I am hardly surprised that you are ashamed of it. Was it common, this practice?'

'I am not sure. There is much debate as to the numbers involved, though the Progressives almost certainly exaggerate. They say it was tens of millions. I doubt whether it was more than thousands. But there is no doubt that the killing of unborn babies has done much to harden attitudes against industrialisation.'

We tried to move into the nave, but it was packed. Our whispering had caught the attention of some worshippers, who frowned and who studied Abdul with some deliberation. But they were not distracted for long, because their attention was soon drawn to the central part of the service: the public confession. This is a new practice and one which seems alien to the very few elderly folk who remember church services from their younger day. Two chairs are put out at the front, on one of which sits the priest and on the other of which sit members of the congregation in turn. We were placed a long way back, and the sound did not travel well, but we asked Abdul to cock his ear and listen:

'I slept with my husband's brother,' one woman was sobbing. 'Not once, but twice. It was such a silly thing, but I have been left at home a lot lately, and I suppose I was bored. I have been close to my partner's brother for a long time, and I suppose there's kind of been something going between us all the time. I was tempted. I was wrong, but I did not mean it. I know that in the Lord's eyes I am an adulterer and that this will count against me when he comes to take his vote on who might be admitted to the afterlife. But I pray that this little mistake in an otherwise blameless life be forgiven.'

At this point the congregation began baying. They were disgusted. 'Shame on you,' I heard one man say. 'Slut!' cried a woman at the front. 'Slut, slut, slut!' The priest, though, was calmer. After allowing them several seconds to express themselves, he motioned the congregation to lower their voices, and then asked, in a tone which was a little reminiscent of the broadcasters of the industrial age: 'How do you feel?'.

'Ashamed and unworthy. On my life I won't do it again.'

The congregation jeered her and she hardly dared to look up. She sobbed, before being led back to her seat in the congregation, where she was surrounded by dirty faces full of hate. She was followed by a freckled-faced young man who confessed to 'unhealthy desires' for a male friend, and drew still more anger from the congregation, who began to stamp their feet. An elderly man then came forward to declare that he had foolishly allowed his thoughts to wander and had daydreamed of riding in a car. 'Please, Lord, forgive me my unclean thoughts and look upon me favourably when it comes to my Recycling.' 'Recycling', I might explain, is a term which has come to be used for the passage of the soul into the afterlife. Next came a serious young lady with protruding chin who declared that for the past two weeks she had been guilty of an unpardonable sin. 'Forgive me,' she said, her eyeballs bulging. 'But I have become tolerant. I have tried to maintain my faith, but I have slipped. I have become lazy and tolerant.'

I nudged Abdul in the arm. 'What do you make of it?' I asked.

'Tolerant? What does she mean?' he said.

'It is a strange word. She means she has allowed profane thoughts to overcome her, become too eager to give consideration to ideas which conflict with her faith.'

'Your people seem so full of apology,' he said. 'Will these several hundred people all go up to make their confessions?'

'Not today. There would not be time. About half a dozen will have their turn today. Each will sit in that chair for quarter of an hour or so, and then the congregation will vote on their redemption. One by one, they will be allowed to go until there is just one left; who will be tied to the railings outside the church and pelted with rubbish. Do you recognise the influence behind this kind of service?'

'No, I do not.'

'If you had watched television during the industrial age, I am sure you would see the similarities. It is the format of the television game show, but with frivolity replaced by hellfire. It is strange that so grave a scene can be traced to the facile entertainments of the industrial age, but it is the way with so many things these days.'

As the congregation began to chant their disapproval at the wretched woman's confession, and then noisily to pray for her, we left. The morning would bring a challenging a journey and we would need our rest. We took a little turnip spirit as a nightcap and sank beneath our duvets: great puffed-up bags of fluff which we have retained as one of the few comforts left over from the industrial age. The night was clear and calm, though our dreams were anxious ones.

4

We left by the back gate, across the open sewer that used to be known as the River Cam. Much of the city's domestic refuse now finds its way into this stream, plus the odd bloated and whitened corpse. These bodies may belong to people who drowned during a flood, who were murdered or who simply took themselves down to the river to die; for some it has become a religious act, to offer themselves to the water. When people do take themselves to the river to die, however, it is almost certain that it usually because they were mortally ill. What is very rare these days is for healthy people to take their lives prematurely. While the end of the industrial age caused great upheaval and caused many to commit suicide in desperation, this act has now become much rarer than it was during the industrial age. People have few expectations of life these days, and so it is much more difficult for them to suffer disappointment.

However they got there, the corpses in the river are a health hazard, and one which causes people to avoid living in houses next to the river. Things are not as bad, however, as they were a year or two ago. To give him his due, Julius Holder is establishing some kind of order in matters of health and sanitation. He has appointed a patrolman and promised punishment for those who

pollute the river: the local bishop has indicated that the owner of
any corpse found dead in the water will be ex-communicated. This
has had some effect, and won praise for Holder. Those who know
nothing of the industrial age assume that rivers were then full of the
bodies of poor souls poisoned by the toxic waters, and believe it is
only now that is progress being made in cleaning the waters.

It was a matter upon which Bump picked up as we made our
way along the river bank past a ghostly form in a plastic coat
washed up against the arches of Kings' College bridge. 'How
could people have been so callous in the industrial age as to leave
the dead to decay in this way?' he asked. 'It is as if you were so
wrapped up in your own little worlds of private achievement and
private accumulation that you barely noticed the suffering. The
cult of individualism was disgusting.'

'But, Bump,' I said. 'You are mistaken. Corpses have only
begun to appear in rivers in recent years. The industrial age was
wholly intolerant of scenes of death. It was not at all unusual to go
through life without ever seeing a dead human being.'

'But what about the bodies which lay about the streets of
London?' said Abdul. 'Believe me, they are legendary. They are
part of the tale of the industrial age that is taught in my country:
we have many, many photographs to prove what I am saying. The
dead bodies wrapped in rags over which you had to step to go
about your business. Are you denying that they existed?'

'You are talking about the homeless,' I said. 'No, I am not
denying that they existed. But they were living people. Were they
to die, they would quickly be taken away. No, they were certainly
not dead. It is odd that they should have acquired such notoriety,
because if you came across one of these homeless people
nowadays, you would not think them the least bit out of the
ordinary: the way we live now is quite close to the way that the
homeless of the industrial age used to live.'

'Except that there was the luxury of hot air vents in those days,'
said Olga.

'Hot air vents, what were these?' asked Abdul.

'The grilles through which hot air was expelled from the underground railways,' I said. 'They were a great comfort to those who had to sleep out of doors. They survive only in mythology: there are people who believe hot air vents were of volcanic origin – and who believe they still exist; it is just a case of looking for them.'

'I cannot stand the way that you romanticise the industrial age,' said Bump. 'It was a terrible time to be alive. So, a few people prospered, but they prospered on the backs of those millions who ended up homeless.'

'I think you will find that they were rather less numerous than the records suppose,' I said. 'The reason so much was made of them was that they were the exception to the comfortable life-styles that many of us enjoyed. So much was made of the homeless precisely because there were so few of them. As a result, they have lived on as myth: to the point at which many people these days believe that most people slept rough.'

We sped by on our skateboards, past many more college lawns which, like ours, have been carved into allotments. The riverside itself is still lined with punts, though these are no longer used as playthings: they ply the river, as far as nearby villages, heavily laden with vegetables. A certain amount of local trade persists, in spite of the Progressives' distaste for trade over long distances. It is considered acceptable to trade with people who reside at up to half a dozen or so miles away, the distance from which a man can comfortably walk to and from in a day; indeed, Cambridge would have starved on several occasions had it not been for outsiders coming to the city, by boat or laden with backpacks, to sell food. But it is not considered right to have contact with people who live further afield. Most people these days pass their lives within the space of a few miles, prevented from travelling further by an invisible cordon of fear: besides the danger of contracting infectious disease, it is widely believed that to travel for more than two hours will bring upon fatal cramps. 'Have you not heard of the aeroplane passengers who were slaughtered in this way by their thousands?' I have often been asked when questioning this.

Across the river, out of the light mist, rose the great stone edifice of the building that is now widely known as the 'tithe barn'. Inside its cool walls are said to be stacked the city's accumulated food reserves; enough grain and turnips, supposedly, to keep the populace fed for 18 months. This is often doubted; some whisper that they do not believe there to be any food in the building at all. It is impossible for an ordinary citizen to find out, for the building is guarded by ruthless characters who, oddly to elderly eyes, wear cassocks. They adopted this uniform because it is what they found lying around; the building in question having formerly been King's College Chapel.

We saw nobody until we reached the plashy wastes above the old mill race. There, the silence was disturbed by a commotion involving a couple of dozen people. We could not make out the scene at first, but as we approached we began to see the outline of a figure who had been tied to a post and, amid much shouting, was being pelted with hard objects: nuts and bolts as it turned out. As we came close it became clear that the figure was the adulterer whom we had seen in church the previous evening, and whose face was now running with blood.

I shouted at the gang and threatened to report them to Julius Holder. They stopped, and turned, exchanged a few words and then broke up, some hiding their faces. The adulterer was left screaming. Before they left, two of the gang recognised Bump and came over to him, incredulous that he could be in such company.

'Where are you being taken?' asked one of them, a fleshy boy with a piece of animal bone through his nose: progressive youths having taken to wearing bones as a mark of virility. Bump blushed.

'We're going fishing,' said Bump. 'Down on the meadows.'

The youth spat in Bump's face, and went away with his

accomplices. When they had gone, we took the unfortunate adulterer back to her home and resumed our journey. On our way, Bump revealed that several of the gang had been his friends and told us how they were in the habit of spending their time. 'We smash bicycles and computers,' he said. 'We throw bricks through plate glass windows of old commercial buildings. We visit old libraries and rip books apart at the spines. . . .'

And, he added, they went dancing. Bump told us that once a week, unknown to his mother, he would slip out of the house late in the evening to join a hastily-assembled crowd on Regent Street. Had we not witnessed the dancing there? As it happened I had once come across this spectacle, and a disturbing sight it was. Perhaps two hundred youths, perhaps more, had gathered, semi-naked. They wore neckerchiefs and carried long sticks which they twirled and bashed with great force. It showed similarities to the Morris dancing which was revived as a piece of pageantry in the industrial age; yet it was much rougher, much more serious. It was also influenced by a touch of the disco and club dancing of the industrial age. The atmosphere was at once violent and sexual. From a distance of 100 feet I was overtaken by an overpowering air of sweat; the natural odours of the body are encouraged by the participants, who do not wash for days before a dance. Encircled by a crowd of whistling, hand-clapping, footstamping onlookers – there was no music as such – the dancers raised their arms, shook their torsos, then disappeared in a swirl of flailing sticks. The boys then paired with girls, some of who were barely beyond puberty but who within a year or two would almost certainly be bearing babies. Then, suddenly, as a diversion, a boy would be brought into the circle, be stripped naked and be pelted with eggs.

'The gay,' said Bump. 'We all hate being the gay, but lots are drawn and we have no choice. But unless you happen to be him, the bashing of the gay is always the most popular part of the dance.'

'Why do you do this?' asked Alferris. 'Who is the gay?'

'The gays?' said Bump. 'Surely you know who they were. They were a suicide cult which emerged at the end of the industrial age, and advocated the extinction of the human race through refusing to breed. By beating the gay we are helping to make ourselves fertile. After beating the gay, somebody is selected as the "pharmacist" and dressed in a white coat. The pharmacist is the one who tried to stop babies being born by forcing people to take pills and potions. His plan was to extinguish the human race, and he very nearly succeeded. That is why there are so few young people compared with very old people: the pharmacist all but stopped mankind from breeding. So we pelt the pharmacist with eggs in order to undo his work, to flush the chemicals from our bodies and make us fertile again.'

We skated on in silence across Coe fen, a patch of open ground which was once used as a playground for Cambridge folk but which has now returned to the wild. The grass has long given way to brambles and hawthorn bushes, which all but conceal the remnants of children's swings. The old ecological textbooks promise that one day abandoned patches of land such as this will eventually turn into oak forest, but I am afraid we will have to endure thistles and brambles for several more decades yet.

Behind the morass of weeds we could just make out the houses of the abandoned suburb of Newnham. These few streets of dirty red brick houses were a noted community of learned folk before the dangers of the present age forced scholars to retreat to the safety of their colleges. What is left is a scene of dereliction typical of most suburbs; the decline of population has driven survivors either to the centres of towns or else to the countryside. Bushes sprout from Newnham's chimney pots. A lorry, its tyres perished and burst, stands in a sullen pose in the road, oozing oily and dreadfully toxic fluids from what you imagine to be stab wounds from its under-belly. There is a softness to the houses, whose roofs and walls are heavily-mossed and look like something from a romantic's garden. Slates have slid from the roofs; through the resulting holes the odd pigeon will emerge to swoop across the street. Many windows have been shattered by pebbles flung from youths' catapults. If you stare through the windows you will often catch pairs of bright eyes, belonging to the dogs and cats who are now the masters of these suburban homes. From one house we heard loud panting; we did not dare investigate further, for dogs are no longer the docile creatures who, save for the odd ill-tempered encounter in the park, spent the industrial age in a state of civilisation. They live in packs which on occasions will come into towns to attack and feed off their former masters. It is probable that the beasts are merely returning to the behaviour of their wolfish ancestors, but that is not how many people see it. Rather they take a look at a dog, they cower and they exclaim: 'it was the industrial people who created these mutant beings. It was an experiment which went wrong, and now we all pay the price!'

The detritus of the industrial age is proving strangely uneven in its ability to withstand time. Decay has come quickly to the cars, whose bodies, holed with rust, resemble the shells of snails who ventured too far out onto the tarmac and were pecked to death by birds. Rust, too, has felled the electricity cables, which now line the ground like giant worms. As a scholar I am only too aware of how the books, newspapers and documents are crumbling: much more quickly, I have noticed, than documents printed on the less acidic paper produced before the industrial age.

Yet some industrial manufactures have proved much hardier. It would be easy to survey the landscape and conclude that the wealth and artistic expression of industrial peoples revolved entirely around plastic bags. They are everywhere, these hateful receptacles, as fresh as the day they were made. Often, they are seen as a curse: find a plastic bag buried in a field and it is said that no edible food will ever grow in that soil again; unless, that is, a ceremony of decontamination is performed – usually at dawn, and led by a priest. But this does not prevent many people, less guided by Progressive principles, from putting plastic bags to practical use.

Enter any house today and you will see them employed for just about every purpose. They are used to preserve food, or are stuffed into holes in windows to keep the weather out. They are used, too, for cooking, especially among older people, who boil birds in them: brought up on convenience food, it is the only way they know how to cook. Plastic bags are even used, I am afraid, as a means of exacting punishment: in some corners of rural England wrongdoers are suffocated by having plastic bags tied over their heads, while crowds look on.

Another common relic of the industrial age was reflecting the early morning sun, and so caught Abdul's attention. 'Those are genuine patio doors,' he said, going up to them and brushing them as if they were a work of art. 'They are amazing, so well preserved. It interests us greatly, the hermetical-sealing of the industrial age house. It is believed that there were people who used to pass straight from their homes to their motor-cars to their offices and back again, and in this way used to go for months without exposure to the outdoors. We cannot understand how it arose, this great fear of the natural world. In the same way you would not drink water from a stream nor eat food which had not been subjected to sterilization. We have read in the textbooks of people who were persecuted for selling foods which had not been subjected to the decreed levels of decontamination, or for building houses which were not sufficiently sealed from the outside world. They were fined and jailed these people, and for what? It is quite obvious to us that your phobia was not going to do you any good. Once your stomachs became accustomed to sterile food and water, it was no longer possible for you to eat or drink anything else. You put yourself at the mercy of your food factories.'

We left behind the final, scattered houses of Cambridge, and went on, unchallenged by the authorities whom we suspected may have spied upon our departure. Soon, it may become impossible to leave Cambridge as we did. There are said to be proposals to build gates around the city to keep it free from unwanted outsiders. A start has even been made on a crudely-built city wall: a row of houses facing Jesus Green has been demolished and the rubble piled high to create a barricade. It is hard, though, to say whether this is part of a coherent strategy to fortify the city or simply an attempt to create work for its own sake. The virtue of physical work is a central tenet of the belief system of the Progressives: soft living, they insist, wrecked industrial man and robbed him of his purpose. They look upon the skinny models of the industrial era – whose photographs still dangle from several clothes shops in the city and are believed to be representative of how industrial people looked – with pity. 'Look at them!' they say. 'How enfeebled people became without physical work!'

It was relief when we reached the meadows which mark the edge of Cambridge. The day was dry, and a smell of spring hung over the narrow pathway. Our spirits were up, but we had two days' walking ahead of us before we would reach the promised railway service at Stevenage, and we would need to pass the time. I had an idea.

'We all have our own reason for making the journey to London,' I said. 'Perhaps we could all take our turn to explain how we came to be here. Mother of Bump, might you begin?'

5

'Me? I was born in the great before, I was,' began Mother of Bump. 'But only just. I suppose I was nine or ten when it all happened, but then counting isn't my strong point, you understand. It's no surprise really that I should have survived these tough times, because I was born out of doors and lived much of my childhood in conditions which weren't that much different from what we have today.

'My dad was a revolutionary, you see, and lived the life of a nomad. He was an anti-globalisation protester, and so he travelled the world, as it was possible to do in those days. He would try to disrupt an economic summit in South America, throw himself in front of the bulldozers trying to dig the channel for an oil pipeline in Africa. Then he would come home and find something to protest about on his own doorstep. He dragged the whole family around the country with him, living in tents. We always lived on the site of the latest road he didn't want built or the latest crops he didn't wanted planted. So I've been everywhere.

'They used to despise my dad at first, the ordinary people who lived in houses. But when you go about the countryside now you realize he was right, wasn't he. It was a right waste of time, building all those roads. There's nothing travelling on them at all, unless you count the odd skateboarder, and you hardly need six lanes of tarmac for that, do you? I suppose my dad was just a little before his time.

'That's not to say I share his philosophy exactly. I mean I've got a bit of a soft spot for cars, to tell you the truth. When you look at all those old photographs they look quaint, don't they, the cars. I should have liked to have a ride in one of them, you know; though you daren't say that sort of thing today, daren't you. When I was a girl I used to dream of growing up and driving around in a fast car. I used to imagine owning a posh house and the like. I right rebel I was, at one stage. One night I ran away with a boy and we tried to break into a car, see if we could get it going – joyriding, it used to be called. It was the closest I got to having a ride. But the car wouldn't start. My dad came and found us, and I was beaten. We never tried it again. Then, as I grew up, I lost my rebelliousness, and I began to see the world more as my dad did. I became conventional. I joined the struggle against what used to be called the global capitalist system.

'I can still see him now, my dad. Skinny, bearded man with a big spot on his neck with hairs growing out of it. He wore a flak jacket which he had picked up in an army surplus store, as they used to call them. He smoked all kinds of weeds, rolled up in little bits of newspaper. And he smelt like a bonfire. They used to call him Moonshine, which was a funny old name really, because shininess wasn't exactly his strong point. Scuffed shoes, tarnished ear-rings: that was more his sort of thing.

'He was a great climber, my dad. He spent a lot of his time up in the trees from what I can remember. But then that was their way, those environmental protesters. They used to live up in the branches for months on end, so the road-builders couldn't cut them down. There were times as a child when I thought he was an ape, because that's what the other children told me he was, and you don't think like an adult when you're a child, do you.

'They're called revolutionaries now, people like my dad. Or

terrorists. Or romantics, that's the other word. They're worshipped for bringing about a revolution against industrialisation. But do you know what? My dad wouldn't have had anything to do with these Progressives. Nothing at all. If it was a revolution that my father was leading, then the revolution's gone sour. He didn't want none of this feudalism, none of this serving your lord, none of this having to seek permission whenever you want to do something. He just wanted to stop the suffering in the world and stop those men in hard hats ruining the environment. But then that's what always happens with revolutions, isn't it: they get taken over by the wrong sort of people. It's all very well making heroes of the environmental protesters of old, but what's happened to them now? Mostly dead, aren't they, or forgotten. The people who are in charge now: well, I'd like to know what some of them were doing when my father was doing his protesting. They were fully paid-up members of the industrial system, that's what I reckon.

'What was I doing when it all happened? I was living not far from here. There were engineers trying to build a road out to a great housing estate outside Cambridge. They called it 'overspill' in those days. I ask you! What a peculiar name for somewhere to live: an overspill settlement. They didn't have much pride in their people in those days, did they: to talk of people spilling all over the place. It was as if they were embarrassed there were so many people alive. It was little joy when a babe was born in those days: it was more like: "oh, no, not another blighter who's going to overcrowd the country and want a little semi-detached house built in the countryside." Funny way to think, if you ask me. And so different from today; you find me a man these days who isn't desperate to spread his seed. In the old days people used to make such a fuss about sex. You used to get all these magazines telling you how to do it. Do it this way; no, do it that way. Have you tried this, have you tried that? Films were full of it – you were lucky if you could watch television for five minutes without seeing writhing buttocks and the like. Oh, people were obsessed with sex in those days, alright. But when it come to the actual breeding, they weren't so good at that, were they? Babies were a right nuisance as far as they were concerned. People used to see babies as a threat to their lifestyle, didn't they? They saw it as a straight choice between babies and consumer goodies. And over time it became less and less of a contest: it was the goodies that usually won. Now babies just happen, and that's that. The idea of stopping them happening just doesn't occur to people, does it?

'Anyway, my dad and his sort didn't like this overspill settlement one bit, so they set up a camp in the way. People could bloody well go and spill over somewhere else, he kept on saying, they're not ruining this countryside. My dad and his accomplices started to dig a network of tunnels beneath the site of this new road, so close to the surface that if you ran a bulldozer over the top the tunnel would collapse and bury anyone who happened to be inside. And then my dad and his accomplices went and lived in the tunnels. He was saying to the builders: "come and kill us if you dare". But they didn't dare. Looking back from this day and age it sounds odd behaviour on the part of the builders, to spare the lives of the protesters, doesn't it, but in spite of the curmudgeonly attitude to babies, life was a lot more sacred in those days.

'What usually happened on these occasions was that the builders would bide their time a bit, and then one morning they'd send the police in to chuck out all the protesters. It was a kind of game, and everyone knew the rules. Normally, the authorities would take a few months before they would come and chuck us off our protest sites. But on this occasion the authorities just didn't come. There was no explanation or anything. They just didn't turn up. We were getting quite bored, to tell the truth. We thought, "come on, we've done our bit, why don't you get on with it?" Several months went by, and you can imagine what the hygiene was like, with several hundred of us all cooped up in this makeshift camp.

We were getting ill, some of us. And still the road-builders wouldn't assert themselves.

'My Dad and his accomplices couldn't have timed their protest better. Though they couldn't have predicted it, the protest coincided with the beginning of the economic troubles. The road-builders never arrived because, like so many commercial organisations, they had gone bust. You can see how far they got in building their road even now, because the tarmac comes to an abrupt halt. It would mean nothing to most people these days, this bit of dead-end road, but to me it is part of history.

'The economic troubles changed matters completely. They called it recession at first, then a slump, then a depression. Then they ran out of words to describe it. There was always some crisis back in the industrial age; it was crises which kept the industrial system rolling along. But this was different. The economy was so bad that it sparked mass dissent against the industrial system – if a system it ever was. Our camp doubled, quadrupled in size: the irony being that it was becoming a housing estate of its own kind. We had all sorts: people who wanted to stop the genetically-modified crops being planted, people who didn't want animals being experimented upon, people who wanted to stop the exploitation of the poor, people who were convinced that manufacturing industry was a devious scheme to kill us off by giving us cancer. But there was one thing which united us all. We wondered: isn't there some simpler, better way of life? There was a disease called 'stress' upon which afflicted a lot of us badly. I was never quite sure what it was: I suppose the best way of describing 'stress' is excessive use of the brain. A brain has only got so much room for thoughts. When you get too many they bounce around the inside of the head and give you terrible pains. That's what people say it was, anyway.

'Once it got into the mind, this negative attitude towards industrialisation, there was no shifting it. It was hysteria if you ask me. The television helped it spread. It was said there was some little device in television sets which was programmed to brainwash people who watched it. I was never sure whether this was true or not, but people keep repeating it even today.

'There was a lot of violence at the end of the industrial age; a lot of vandalism and a lot of noisy protest. Though these made a great spectacle, the real damage was caused by something quite different: people stopped buying things. Riots were never going to ruin industrial civilization. Quite the reverse: all they did was create work, jobs and profits for the people employed to clear up the mess. But when people decided they didn't want to play ball any more, didn't want to spend their money? How was industrial civilization supposed to cope with that? The truth is, it couldn't. The economists used to take it for granted that we were all naturally greedy creatures: 'consumers', they called us, as if all we ever did was sit with our mouths open, waiting for them to be stuffed. The moment we stopped consuming, however, the end was inevitable.

'The great consumer strike started with people boycotting products which they said were poisoning the environment and ruining the climate. They started to shun imports from China, saying that they were bringing deadly diseases into the country. They started refusing to take pills and medicines because they were tested on animals, or because they said the doctors had purposely designed these pills to turn people into idiots. I've no idea whether these things were true or not, but there was no shortage of people coming forwards with 'victims', like children who had turned berserk after they had taken some pill or other. The doctors refuted it all, but then they would, wouldn't they? One thing was for sure: doctors and the ordinary people were never going to understand each other, because they didn't speak the same language. What was that special language which the doctors and scientists used to speak to each other? Begins with a 'j'. Jargon, that's it. I never spoke of word of it myself; I just knew it as the devil's tongue.

'The first ones to suffer when the economy slumped were the borrowers, who had their homes repossessed. But savers weren't far behind. I suppose it had always taken a leap of faith, to put your money in a bank. But when the transactions were reduced to little electronic bleeps, and the computers which ran the banks kept failing, it started to verge on foolishness. Whatever it was, the people did for the system because they kept taking money out of the banks out of fright. Banks could cope with their computers breaking down, but this was the one thing they couldn't cope with: people coming in droves and asking for their money. It soon turned out that there wasn't much to a bank beyond the plastic and glass façade, and a bit of loose change in the tills. They were built out of hope, those banks, nothing more. The electronic money simply vanished into thin air. We were left with the grubby notes and coins, but they, too, aren't much welcomed these days, are they.

'The lack of confidence in the currency spurred on us protesters no end. Before we knew it, we were fighting several battles at once. We went with some farmers and blocked off the road at the north of Cambridge where all the lorries brought in food from Europe. The public had taken a dislike to food coming in from abroad, saying it was causing disease and killing off the animals and crops on our own farms. Once again, people from the nice houses came to support us. They cheered us from the motorway bridges. It is all the fault of these imported industrial goods they said: it is thanks to them that we have all lost our jobs! They call it "muck", now, don't they, the piles of old industrial goods which occasionally turn up in half-buried lorry containers: "foreign muck".

'I don't know who set alight the first lorry. Many names have been bestowed upon the martyrs who were said to have begun the assault on foreign muck, but I don't recognise any of them. I think they have all been made up. All I remember are the scenes. Before long, the whole road was blazing and the sky filled with black, oily smoke. Apocalyptic, they called it in all the papers. They loved it, the journalists. But they didn't really believe this was the end of industrial civilisation; like so many people at the time, they just couldn't take the threat seriously. Most people had only ever known comfortable times and couldn't imagine what revolution was really like. And besides, the anti-industrial protests lacked a single, straightforward cause. They were a mass of contradictions; everyone wanted to have their little stab against authority, but had no real idea where it was leading.

'There were still those who wanted to carry on with their normal jobs as if nothing had happened, hoping the economy would recover. We thought them mad. But we did have one thing in common with them. None of us understood how this global economy worked. The art of survival in those days was not the straightforward business it is now: when you see a wild cow, you kill it and eat it. When you were hungry in the industrial age you went and bought something in a plastic bag, and you had no idea where it had come from or how it had got to you. And that offended lots of people, that did, made them feel insecure. That was the one thing the industrial economy didn't offer: security. Because people didn't understand how the economy worked, they feared it.

'With more people arriving by the week, we soon outgrew our camp. With a lot of farms going bankrupt, we saw our chance and seized some land up in the fens. We arrived at dawn one morning, destroyed the machinery, blocked the roads and made the land ours. There was no physical resistance to us, just the threat of legal action. People say nowadays that lawyers were great oppressors, don't they – but don't you believe a word of it. The law was like a plodding bear: it would catch up with you in the end, but it was comical how long it took. While the lawyers were spinning things out so as to increase their fees, we got away with our squatting.

'There was this romantic notion at the time: someone had noticed there were about as many people in Britain as there were

acres, and they thought, what if we could all have our own acre,
do away with the industry and go back to the land? It got big, that
idea: "give us back our acre," people used to say. It was horribly
impractical, of course, the idea of all the land in Britain being
lotted out at an acre per person, but that didn't bother the
romantics. Industrial civilisation, as people used to say, was very
good at feeding people and keeping them warm, but it had no
heart and had no soul. People were fed up of their little lives,
that's what; they wanted to be forced to live.

'It was all romance, though, just dreams. Most of these
romantics hadn't got the first idea about husbandry, and neither
had we. We worked our backs off, we did, but we were quite
unprepared for the disciplines of farming. We got better at it, but
it took time. At first we were always arguing about what we were
going to do. They went on for days, these arguments: people
shouting, grabbing each other by the throat, and drinking until
they passed out. We were supposed to be against all this packed
food, you understand, but that didn't stop cans of beer finding
their way onto the farms. We had some of the best soil in the land,
we did: pure black peat which you could run through your hands
like flour. Yet what we got out of it didn't do it justice, I tell you.
We never got anything planted at the right time, and half of what
we grew was eaten by insects. But we couldn't bring ourselves to
blame our methods: rather we used to say the soil had been ruined
by the chemicals used in industrial agriculture and it needed time
to recover. That was our excuse. People are still using that excuse
now. But it isn't true, I reckon. And you know what, I miss all
that chemical food, I do. I tell you what, food just doesn't taste the
same without all the chemicals, does it. I remember when food
used to melt in your mouth. You hardly had to chew it, not like
the bread and vegetables we have to eat now. We've become like
cows: condemned to spend so much of our lives chewing that it
doesn't leave much time for anything else.

'Because we couldn't get enough to eat, we started to raid the great steel warehouses where food used to be stored in those days. We would prise open their doors with iron bars and help ourselves to what was inside. We treated the contents of the warehouses as common property. Communism, some people called it, but they were wrong. We weren't into communism. We treated the land as our property and defended it as such. We didn't allow anyone else on it, and fought them off with sticks on many occasions. These days, they talk as if the revolution was a glorious time, but for those of us caught up in the thick of it, it was a dirty struggle.

'In time, though, we did start taking refugees from the cities into our community. There was an outbreak of flu at the time, which people blamed upon the Chinese. Thousands had died in the cities, and many of those who survived made a dash to the countryside. They became so numerous that it became impossible to keep them away, so we made use of them instead. They drove up in battered cars, laden with possessions: much of it which they didn't really own because they were in debt to the banks. There was much unrest over this. The police – this was when there still were police, before their wages were stopped – kept coming and asking questions, then taking a lot of the stuff away. It was an illusion, most people's wealth. When you took away all the things they had bought on borrowed money, they hardly had anything left.

'A lot of the people who came to join us out of desperation were lost souls. I remember the family that pitched up next to us; they'd been travelling round looking for work – he used to sell insurance or something – but because there was no work they came round to the idea of living off the land. They came full of it, this family: boasting of how they were going to roll up their sleeves and join in. It was as if they were on a camping holiday. They were into good neighbourliness. They wanted to organise everything, tidy the place up, dig holes every time they wanted a shit. They didn't understand that we were an itinerant community, and we didn't mind trashing the place because we

would soon be moving on. They used to talk about the
environment as if it was their living room, where nothing was
allowed to be out of place. And as for the kids, they kept wailing
all day and all night for their lost comforts. Then one of the kids
caught one of these diseases that was going round, and they rushed
round like mad trying to find a doctor, but the kid died. That
took the wind out of their sails. Terrible it was, to see people like
this: clever people incapacitated by the shock of losing their
comfortable lives.

'But the ones who fled the cities for the country were the
relatively lucky ones. The ones who stayed behind did themselves
no favours at all. People were found shaking with hunger in their
houses in the posh parts of London, completely at a loss as to what
to do. That's what happened, you see: people were so out of
touch with the basic arts of survival that they were helpless when
the shops emptied. And panic emptied them quick. There are still
houses with cupboards stashed with rusting tins of food left over
from the last days of the industrial age – houses where someone
had squirreled away what they thought was enough food to last
them years, then had died of something else.

'There was a lot of death and disease in our camp – much of
which we blamed on the Chinese flu, though it probably didn't
really come from such an exotic location. It was probably just
ordinary dysentery. But it was nothing compared with what came
later. At this stage it was still cancer, which carried off my mother,
that was our biggest fear. It was invariably blamed upon the
industrial poisons said to be floating around in the air. "It was the
dust in the office where I used to work 30 years ago," people used
to say as they went down clutching their sides in agony. "I knew
it would kill me in the end." You know how it is now: it's a
privilege to live long enough to get cancer, but in those days
cancer was the biggest fear there was.

'There was still a government at this stage, but increasingly it
lost control of the great refugee camps. Occasionally, the

Government would attempt to wrest back control by sending in the Army – this was when there was just the one army, before it broke up into hundreds of militias. The Army would spray us with disinfectant, to stop us spreading infectious disease. But it caused horrible anger, it did. Started riots. Until this time, the government had tolerated the "back to the land" thing – in fact secretly the Government loved it because it cut the welfare bill and saved the state from going bankrupt for a year or two. But now the Government started trying to contain us, stop us moving about and stop our numbers growing. That's what the spraying was really about. You'd see these tiny specks in the sky. Then they'd get bigger, and before you knew it a plane would be overhead, raining all this disinfectant on you. We were stunned at first. We didn't know what had hit us.

'But we fought back. We weren't going to mind our own business any longer. There were some of us who started burning the factories, bombing the offices. What we did was spread a rumour that such and such a factory was leaking a lethal new poison into the atmosphere, and then we would go and destroy it. There were plenty of people happy to see the back of these polluting factories, never mind what they thought of us otherwise.

'Of course there was a limit to how much havoc we could cause by ourselves. But the authorities made it so much worse for themselves because they were so obsessed with public safety. That's what I reckon, anyway. You only had to explode one bomb and everything got closed down: the roads, the trains, the shops. "Security reasons", that's what they always used to say. We didn't even need to block the roads in the end; the authorities would do our work for us. I don't suppose we would have been able to achieve what we did had it not been for the speed at which bad news travelled. We had our brickbats and petrol bombs, but the real weapon against industrialisation was sitting in the corner of everyone's front room. Pure terror, the telly. The news was always so depressing and so relentless that it destroyed people's hope. In the industrial age people theoretically were happier, healthier and richer than they had ever been. But you wouldn't guess from looking at their great long faces.

'Short of shutting yourself in a hole in the ground, there was no getting away from bad news back in the industrial age. I don't think our minds ever really learned to cope with the flood of information to which we were subjected. You would find yourself anxious about something that was going on half a world away. You couldn't stop yourself sweating, or sobbing. Some went further: threw themselves under trains because they couldn't bear to know what was going on. In the end, it was corrosive – the telly killed off our ability to feel good about the world. It was a time of great cleverness, the industrial age. Oh, a very clever time, it was. Trouble was, it sent us mad.

'It didn't help that we were ageing. We ended up with more and more old people, too crumpled to do any work, and fewer and fewer young people to support them. It didn't add up. It was marvellous, all these sleek cars and planes we had at the end of the industrial age, all these sparkling gadgets. But when you looked at the wrinkly old people using them, they weren't so impressive, were they? We were right crocks compared with our machines.

'There were times when I thought it pure bliss to be living on the land. But over the past few years, it's all turned around, hasn't it. The ideology's all died, as far as I'm concerned. More and more land has fallen into the hands of those sharks that joined the revolution late: the ones who had been industrialists. The rules that these Progressives make aren't about saving mankind or even saving the planet; it's just about keeping themselves in power. I mean, this business about you not being allowed to ride bicycles because they are mechanical, I ask you! You can't use bicycles because they are an industrial product; that's what they say; if you want to cart something around you must use animals. It's madness. What they really mean is they don't want people travelling around because it would weaken their power, that's what I reckon.

'We were camped up in the fens until a year or two back. But the camp was dying, and the Progressive landowners were closing in on us. Our work was getting harder and a lot of us were getting old. We didn't have enough people to keep us in food, and so do you know what we had to do? This is the ironic bit, this is: we had to give up our land and come back into the city just to survive. Sold our freeholds, that's what we had to do. Just to live.

'So ever since, I've had to work for Julius Holder. And I can't recommend that to anybody. It isn't dignified, spit-polishing a man's boots all day. And stitching his trousers: that's not the greatest of jobs, either. A bit hazardous, too, if you ask me, when he refuses even to take them off while you're working on them. I tell you, there was more than once that I was tempted to make a little slip with my needle – accidental of course. No-one would ever have been the wiser. But I just couldn't seem to bring myself to do it. I've been a terrorist in my life, and I've done the most horrible things, but it's funny, we're not drawn to do that sort of thing any more, are we? We're all cowed, aren't we? We are just as oppressed as before, if you ask me, only not by all those unfeeling multinational companies, by the lords on our doorstep. Which is the worst? I'm not sure if I know.

'I wasn't the only one working on Holder's clothes. He was always wanting new outfits. And he had to have everything made from scratch – it was shocking all the lovely old nylons he had chucked out! And as soon as his clothes were done, they always had to be unstitched straight away because he had put on a bit more weight, or he didn't like the cut. There were half a dozen of us stitching and unstitching all day. We hardly saw daylight for half the year. Right little industry, it was. Not that you were allowed to use that word, mind – you'd get rapped across the knuckles. We were craftsmen, that's what we had to call ourselves. Industry is the devil's work as far as Holder is concerned. But if you ask me I'd say he preaches one thing and practises another.

'So that's my story, Professor. Not a great life, I admit. But that's not the point, is it. The point is that I'm still here to tell the tale, and in this day and age that's bordering on an achievement in itself, isn't it?"

6

The day was beginning to congeal as the Mother of Bump finished her tale. A rippled skin had settled over the sky, in which the sun appeared as a sickly curd. They used to be hazy, these sort of days, but no longer. Away from the towns and villages, clear air is one of the few commodities we have gained since the end of the industrial era; from elevated ground it is now usually possible to pick out trees and the skeletal remains of barns thirty, forty miles away, where in the industrial age your view would have been cut off by the petrochemical fug half a dozen miles off. People used to say that the rapid transportation of the industrial age had made the world seem a smaller place, but optically the effect was the opposite: the smog used to make familiar landmarks look further away than they were. Clear air makes the Hertfordshire hills seem within touching distance, even if to travel to them is now a day's work.

Elated by the pleasures of the morning air I turned to the Mother of Bump and said:

'You are quite a peasant, madam.'

I still wince when I use that word, even though it is at least two decades since it ceased to be regarded as an insult and became instead one of the most generous compliments you can pay

somebody, implying that they are possessed with great wisdom
and common sense.

'You have entertained us with charm,' I went on. 'Your tale has
touched us all.'

'It's not as if my hard time has been any harder than anyone
else's hard time, is it?' countered Mother of Bump. 'The truth is,
we've all had it rough these past years. That's if we can't be said to
have had it rough since time immemorial. We're suffering
creatures, aren't we? But you take it from me, there's nothing
special about us lot – not when you consider history and
everything. It's just one constant struggle: that's how my father
saw history. Taken over time it doesn't seem to get any better and
it doesn't seem to get any worse. We're only different because we
were born into a period of plenty. We were brought up to think
that suffering was a thing of the past, but in reality it was just that
there was a backlog of suffering. That's what we've had over the
past few years: a clearance of the backlog. They don't last, do they
Prof, these periods of plenty.'

'They do not.'

'Our suffering's going to be all gone and forgotten soon, isn't?
That's just the way of things. No-one gets too upset about things
which happened so long ago, do they? I mean, when you think of
the cudgels and the bludgeons of ancient history, you don't feel
the pain, do you? And even when you think of those poor young
boys blown sky high in the industrial wars, it only just about hurts,
doesn't it? It's only the suffering since the industrial age that you
really feel, because you think "that could have happened to me",
don't you?'

'There is just one thing troubling us,' I said. 'We still do not
know your name. Would you care to enlighten us?'

'I don't see why I should have to. The truth is I hate my name.
Okay, since you ask, I'll tell you. But how would you feel if you
had a name like Beelzebub?'

There was, in spite of the embarrassment over her name, a

delightful lack of self-consciousness about Mother of Bump. In this she was typical of so many people these days. It is not done to care too much about your accent, your appearance, or even – and this I do regret a little – your personal hygiene. Not only is it seen as natural and normal to smell, a lot of people these days like to be heard belching and to be seen with food hanging off their beards, because it exudes a feeling of well-being.

People do not preen themselves these days; neither do they get anxious that they are overweight or that their hair is untidy. They do not wear jewellery and as for spots, any ruddy eruption is considered to be a sign of rude health. He who has spots is said to be red-blooded and manly: a far healthier condition than to be anaemic, an ailment which is believed to result of the convenience food of the industrial age. Perfumery is a lost art: though richer folk do spray themselves with a kind of scent, this has nothing to do with making themselves attractive to the opposite sex: it is to keep the mosquitoes away. The favoured concoction is a blend of oil and garlic; which people insist on calling 'French dressing', ignorant of the fact that the term originally referred to something with which you used to dress a salad, not yourself.

The only people who show signs of vanity are those old enough to have been adults during the industrial age. It is sad to watch some of these wrinkled old folk sitting around on benches all day long, admiring themselves in bits and pieces of broken mirror and muttering to themselves. One such man I know, a vagabond who was formerly head of a leading advertising agency, spends much time sitting in an old churchyard, looking into his own tired eyes and muttering ceaselessly to bewildered children: 'I must relaunch! I must relaunch!' They simply cannot understand what he sees in himself.

There are old men, too, who insist on wearing tight, bulging shorts to show off their manhood, in spite of having suffered the inevitable shrivelling which accompanies old age. There are elderly ladies who go about with their lardy buttocks split asunder by frayed old pieces of swimwear. Many younger folk, by contrast, go about very well-clothed; sporting several layers of incongruous garments. This is except in high summer, when they are apt to remove the entirety of their clothing. But they do this only to cool down, not to show off their bodies. No longer does the sight of flesh automatically stimulate the sexual appetite; that is considered to be a 20th century perversion.

While many are happy to strip naked in summer to bathe in rivers – the only time many of them wash – on no account will they do so while the sun is shining. It is a popular belief that the powers of the sun were horribly and massively increased by mankind during the industrial age. Some even hold that the sun was created as a result of an atomic experiment which went wrong. Mankind, it is sometimes preached in church, attempted to procure an inexhaustible form of energy, and was punished for his arrogance by being condemned to be fried by the sun for ever after. There are people who watch their skin obsessively for spots, going mad when they discover an enlarged, ruddy mark. They, scream, tear at their spots, splash vinegar upon them – to no avail, for sometimes these cancers turn out to be fatal. In many towns in the last week of June, safely covered head to toe in long shawls, worshippers take to streets for a ceremony to celebrate the point of the year at which the powers of the sun begin to diminish. Several days of feasting follow. There is a more solemn ceremony at the end of December to mark the point at which the sun's strength begins to increase yet again. A long silence is held at this latter ceremony for worshippers to hang their heads in shame at the excesses of the industrial age. Industrial goods – toy cars and aeroplanes are an especial favourite – are presented upon the altar to be smashed with stones.

The threat of cancers did not bother us as we took a break from our journey on the meadows to the south of Cambridge. We all stripped naked and plunged into the weedy waters of Cam. It is when people are stripped that one realises how much the people of today differ physically from those of the industrial era. This is particularly true of the younger folk: when presented with old photographs one is immediately struck how substantially built and yet how fresh-faced young men were 50 years ago; the easy protein of their diet had quickly given them the stature of adults, yet they stayed soft and pasty into adulthood. In photographs, the young of 50 years ago seem like giant babies, sucklings of six foot three. Nowadays young men tend to be willowy; they are much shorter, and their faces are more drawn and creased. Their chests are hollow, and reverberate during attacks of coughing, while their limbs are woody, their tendons standing out like wires. By his stature, Bump, though now sixteen, would scarcely have passed for a twelve year old in the industrial age; his puberty was incomplete and he did not yet reach five feet. Manhood is becoming a later and more brief affair.

Elderly folk have suffered much from changes in diet and the decline of industrial comforts. Many old people have been reduced to insanity by mad cravings for long extinct junk food, and the salt which lurked within it: some have taken to gnawing at fistfuls of salt from the yellow roadside boxes erected in the industrial age to help keep the roads free of ice. Others, who have lost their teeth and must survive on swill, have become yellowed and flatulent. Inland, people suffer from horrible swellings of the neck; a curable disorder but one which requires the sufferer to consume old tins of fish. These tins are very rare, and so it is only the wealthy who can afford the cure. The elderly stand relatively tall compared with the young. Or at least we do if we can stand at all; the poverty of our diet has left us unable to sustain the impressive frames we acquired during more plentiful times, and so we tend to flop forwards, our backbones no longer able to support a great height. It is not uncommon to see people bent like boomerangs; such people can only hold themselves aloft with the aid of sticks. Distorted frames have become so common a feature of the elderly that the standard shape of a coffin is now gently curved.

If people have changed in their physique, the same is even more
true of animals. While bathing in the waters of the Cam, we were
subjected to a terror common in rural parts these days. It began
with a thunderous noise and a cloud of dust. Before we had
chance to emerge from the water we saw that we were being
charged down by a herd of cattle. They came from the west, these
impressive beasts, from the great plains of chalk grassland that
stretch up from Bedfordshire. You who are only used to the
plump, docile cows of the industrial era will have to use some
imagination to picture them: half of them, after all, were not cows
but bulls with spiteful eyes, full-grown horns and testicles which
swung like inverted punch-bags. Their entire sides shuddered
whenever they put their hooves to earth, and long strings of saliva
dribbled from their mouths. The cows, too, seem to have changed
since your day; they are leaner, longer than their ancestors of fifty
years ago; their udders no longer trail along the ground as they did
in the days when they were bred as milking machines. Cattle are
no longer sedentary, but move around constantly, at a fair gallop.
Freed from the constraints of barbed wire, they have gone back to
living in vast herds which sweep the landscape before them,
stripping the country of vegetation as they go about.

You can pass several years without seeing a cow, but when a
herd comes your way it cannot easily be ignored. Cattle do not
stick to the country; sometimes they hustle their way through our
towns, pushing their faces into our dustbins. They are no longer
exclusively herbivores; having acquired a taste for animal protein
during the industrial age they have become scavengers, nosing
around for scraps of fat and the occasional dog or human carcass. It
is said that the town of Stamford a few years ago was decimated –
and later abandoned – thanks to an invasion of cattle which killed
or maimed dozens of unfortunate residents. Seeing the cattle
approach, the residents ventured into the streets armed with sticks
in an attempt to ward them off; but unaware of how vicious these
once-docile animals have become the people stood their ground

and were gored. Those Stamford townsfolk who survived fled to the woodlands. I have seen a map, prepared by a resident of Cambridge on which Stamford is marked with the words: 'Warning: here there are cattle'.

It may have been the same herd which charged us on Grantchester Meadows, for they travel great distances in their search for grass and water. They amassed on three sides of us, then spread themselves out along the waterline, gulping as they went, pushing forwards into the water until their bellies were submerged. They waved their horns at us and would happily have killed us, though we were fortunate in being able to keep just beyond their reach. We waded into the water up to our necks and swam downstream, out of danger. Not so lucky was a boy who had been sitting by the water's edge just by Grantchester and whom, we surmised, had been thrown into the water and trampled underfoot. It was left to Dr Khan to pronounce him dead.

It took little time. Death is not accompanied by the formalities that it used to be. There are tales of people going to their graves alive, so imprecise are the methods of medical diagnosis. In many towns death certificates are still theoretically a requirement, but they are little more than works of fiction. Some of the causes of death now being recorded are dreamed up on the spur of the moment: registrars frequently attribute deaths to 'misery', 'fright', 'arbitrary decision of God' and, a favourite one this, 'consumption', which, ignorantly, is now taken to mean excessive indulgence in food and drink. When elderly people die, Progressive physicians love to place the blame on industrial diseases, some of whose names will be familiar to you: repetitive strain injury, sick building syndrome, irritable bowel syndrome. It is unlikely that the unfortunate subjects of these certificates really succumbed to these disorders; but they are effective in reminding people of the evils of the industrial era.

We buried the Grantchester boy beneath a large pile of mud

and leaves; cremation, which might save communities from disease, is condemned as too industrial a means of disposing of the dead. It is used only as a punishment, for those deemed to have committed heresies against Progressive thought. After the brief ceremony which we awarded the boy, Dr Hoeffel was taken ill. He fell to the ground complaining of chest pains. While he was down his breathing became irregular and his face went white. He was to recover, but while he was down, Dr Khan announced her fear that he had suffered a heart attack. 'He has over-exerted himself by plunging into the cold water,' she said. 'His body is suffering from shock.'

Bump became much annoyed at this. 'To say that cold water is bad for the body? Why, that is nothing more than an old scientists' tale. It is typical of the theories which were spread against nature in the industrial age. We all know the reason why this man is unwell: it is the chemicals which were let loose into the water in the industrial age. He is overcome by the fumes.'

Olga protested bitterly. 'This is foolishness!'

Bump went on: 'People used to believe in science because it gave them simple explanations for things which any wise man would put down to the work of God. It gave them a kind of security I suppose, believing they knew how the Universe began and how their hearts worked. But it was the comfort of fools.'

'You have not the least idea what you are talking about,' said Dr Khan.

'I have heard it all from my teachers. In the industrial age the climate was ruined, the atmosphere was filled with allergens and the water and rocks infused with poisons. You just tell me they weren't! Why, otherwise, are people so sick these days? It will take hundreds of years to recover the lost health of the planet. And it is the same with our own health. There are people I know who cannot even breathe, so bad is the air. I have pains in my sides, and I know why it is. My healer said it is all caused by the bad electrical currents which are still passing through the Earth. Don't you tell me that is not true. My healer has had it revealed to him. What is the term used when God reveals all to us in a vision? "Evidence", that is it. My healer felt my muscles. Then he closed his eyes and said he saw the evidence before him. It was electricity, he said. The pylons left over from the industrial age: they pumped so much electricity into the ground that it is still coming out.'

'I have heard much about these things,' said Abdul. 'The industrial age, I understand, people spent much of their time in ill health.'

'Not at all,' said Olga. 'The health of people during the industrial age was very good. Thanks to the work of the doctors, it was the norm, not an exception, for people to live into their seventies and eighties.'

'But then why,' said a puzzled Abdul, 'when you read magazines from the industrial age, is there always a story about a child struck down with some deadly disease, or a young woman battling with cancer? Why all the pictures, of which there is much in the literature, of people in wheelchairs, or breathing through tubes, attached to machines? If illness was not the common experience, then how come it features in such a big way in industrial culture?'

'You are mistaking the treatments for the disease,' said Olga. 'The people whom you describe were undergoing treatment. They were being made better, or if they couldn't be made better their suffering was being alleviated. Nowadays, they would simply die, and die quickly. In the industrial age we were able to sustain life long after it was able to sustain itself. That is an achievement for which people these days have little regard. We could bombard cancers with radiation, cut open people's chests and repair damaged hearts: it is so terrible that these skills have been lost.'

'The inhumanity of it defies belief,' said Bump. 'The tortures to which people were put through on the pretext of curing them of some disease! The poor people whose bodies were cut open, they were not to know that you were cutting out their souls! The barbarity of it all! And you try to defend all that?'

'I defend my work to the death. And I have been quite prepared to suffer persecution for my belief in an efficient healthcare system. But somebody must stand up for the principles of science.'

'Persecution? That's rich, that is. A scientist is a fine one to complain about persecution.'

'I can tell just by looking at you that you've never been stretched on a rack. You've never had your ankles shackled and your neck wrenched from your shoulders to the point that you can feel your ligaments splintering and your bones straining from their sockets. And it's all so much worse when you're a physician, I tell you, because you know exactly what is happening to you. You can put a name to the traumas being inflicted upon your body.

'And I bet you've never been strapped to a seat and dunked in a freezing river and held there as the weeds stream across your face and the fish brush past your cheeks. You've never had to hold your breath for four whole minutes and felt the flesh around your face go numb as you come round to accepting your death. And then, just as you are about to open the floodgates to your lungs, out they lift you, dripping, drenched. And then they jeer: "a scientist! A scientist!" That's persecution for you.

'And what was my crime, to be treated in so despicable a manner? To have "mocked the creation of life": that was one of the charges put to me. What a thing to accuse me of, especially considering I was only trying to help people!

'I was a doctor, but not one of those who was involved in the day-to-day business of broken bones and damaged hearts. No, my interests were much purer, much more beautiful than that. Genetics was my speciality: I was one of those who helped reduce the human body to digital form. We had every body part, every disease mapped out in code. We could tell virtually anything about your health: we could detect a heart murmur when it was still a faint cry for help, pinpoint cancers when they consisted of just a few cells, and – this is the really clever bit – tell you if you were destined to develop a disease decades before the first symptoms made themselves known. And all I needed was a tiny drop of your blood. Just a pinprick; you could hardly see it. I could have taken the sample from you without you even noticing: that's how powerful the science of genetics was. Not everybody liked the idea, but everyone stood to benefit, for deep down in the genes there is something wrong with everyone. Something mortally wrong. We are all imperfectly built. But the fact was that for the first time in human history we had the chance to do something about it.

'I suppose my critics had one point: genetics did give doctors like myself an lot of power over our patients. There were those who did not want to know their genetic codes, those who thought it sacrilegious to change the course of nature, those who turned into nervous wrecks in my clinic when told what was going on inside their bodies. But let me say I never tried to do anything other than good. My motivation was never anything other than the pursuit of other people's happiness. I was quite unprepared for how people would turn against the medical profession so suddenly and so totally.

'They call it vanity, now, taking an interest in the workings of your body. They think of it as a deadly sin, to overly-concern yourself with your health. Correct bad vision with spectacles, try to remove the bags under your eyes with a little help from the surgeon's knife, and it's eternal damnation: that's what they think these days. Attempt to practise what I used to regard as basic medicine and you will be charged with "interfering with the natural healing processes of the human body". It is an alien idea to me. I am pleased that I was brought up in an age in which people took pride in their bodies, and were prepared to honour them by coming to my clinics.

'Those of us who worked in hospitals were used to being

accused of doing people more harm than good. We were used to patients becoming angry, even violent, when we failed to cure their conditions. Yet nothing prepared us for the appalling episode of history known as the Dissolution of the Hospitals. You may have forgotten the reasons behind this piece of vandalism. Rumour went around that doctors were deliberately releasing fatal viruses and bacteria in our hospitals in order to kill off their patients: even today, there are people who will not go near the sites of old hospitals for fear there are still "superbugs" lurking in the ruins. Besides this, the Progressive lords accused us of playing God. Our genetics' work was said to be an attempt to fashion the human race in our own image. It was said that in hidden laboratories somewhere deep inside our hospitals we were attempting to manufacturing a race of super beings which would one day replace the human race. This is what the thugs came looking for: cadavers, embryos, any sign that we were interfering in the creation of life. Of course, they found nothing which supported their fevered concerns, but this did not stop them from destroying the hospitals. Operating theatres were upturned, monitors and life support machines ripped from the walls and destroyed as "objects of science". But it was the X-ray machines that saddened me most: as they broke them up I asked them why they were doing so, and do you know what they said? They said: this machine is a aid to self-idolatry – it is bad enough to want to admire your own face, but to want to look deeper, to see your insides, this was an insult to the work of God.

'Dozens of my colleagues were murdered in the wards, slain in the operating theatres with their own scalpels. Patients were turned out of their beds – "liberated", as the thugs described it. It did not seem to bother them that many of the patients died in agony soon after being disconnected from the machines which were keeping them alive: the thugs believed they had freed their souls, and that was that. I was seized and would have been killed had the mob not picked me out for a show trial. They wanted to make a spectacle out of the attack on the hospital, to create a mood among the wider population. And so they borrowed a ritual from medieval times, the dunking of witches, and adapted it as their own. I was dragged in my white coat, kicking, screaming all the way to the weir near Queens' College. I was strapped in a chair and forced underwater and subjected to a test which I could not win: drown and I would have been cleared; survive and I would have been convicted of practising science – and burnt. As it was, I survived. When I came up the crowd was wailing. I was insensible. When I came round I could not believe I was still in the heart of this city where but a few years before I had been holding conferences on the advance of medicine.

'They took me, manhandled me, my white coat dripping, my plastic name tag covered with weeds. They took me to a stake. And they would have finished me off had it not been for a group of medical students who, having watched the proceedings, decided to take things into their own hands. Waving syringes filled with their own blood, they charged at the crowd, shouting the names of every mortal disease which came into their heads. In the panic and confusion I escaped.

'A few days later, heavily disguised, I returned to the hospital, to find it partly burned to the ground. I salvaged what I could muster – antibiotics, painkillers – and packed them into a suitcase and fled the city. I took to the back country of the fens, where there was not the fervour there was in Cambridge, and laid low for a while. I found my way to the home of friends, and they concealed me in their attic and fed me, bringing me every day tales of more hospitals that had been over-run and their doctors murdered. It was impossible for me to go out: I could never be sure that I would not run into an old patient who, though he had been thankful at the time of his treatment, had had his mind poisoned by the fervour against doctors and would turn me in. I know of several doctors who were killed in this way. This is what happened at the time of the great terror: Progressives would pick on one group of people at a time: the doctors, the lawyers, the businessmen, and promote violence against them. Then, the job done, they would move onto another group. But it is peculiar how a seemingly irresistible wave of violence can still fail to bring about the extinction of the people it targets. While I was hidden in my attic in the fens, I imagined myself to be the only doctor left alive. But in the years since then I have recognised several others of my colleagues. We have half-stared at each other in the street; we dare do no more than that. I can only assume there must be hundreds of us who somehow escaped the terror.

'In time, the murder spree against doctors declined and I took to the occasional walk from my hiding place. It was into a rapidly changing world that I emerged: the cars had all but gone, the electric lights went out one by one. But as far as my safety was concerned, my walks passed without incident. Day by day, I took to longer walks, and ventured around the village. In time I became integrated into the local society, though I was a person without a past, without an identity beyond the clothes that I was wearing. And I am sure I would have remained that way had it not been for the plague. To this day I cannot be confident of what the plague was – without my petri-dishes, I am guessing – but I am quite sure it was nothing to do with the bubonic plague around which its mythology was built. More likely it was a water-borne disease of the type which had afflicted mankind right up until the introduction of a hygienic supply of running water. With that supply now breaking down, people were forced to use wells and ditches once more. The microbes found the perfect host: a people so used to sterile food and drink that their bacterial resistance had become enfeebled through inaction.

'The disease was patchy in its choice of victims: one village might escape, the next lose so many people that it was abandoned. Mine was one of the unlucky ones. I have this inkling that the water, which was collected in buckets from a spring close to an old cattle farm, tasted sweeter that morning, though I may be fooling myself. All I know is this: house after house was consumed by the sound of groaning and whimpering. The sickness took less than 48 hours to do its dreadful work on the digestive system, turning its victims white and making them thirst for the very water which had made them ill in the first place. Without the painkillers they had come to rely upon, many threw themselves down staircases or cut themselves with broken glass to avoid the last writhing hours. In one dreadful night the disease took half my village. The odd confused survivor, weak and dripping with sweat, awoke up to find himself in a scene of biblical horror.

'Me, I survived without the agonies. The moment I saw signs that the sickness had reached our corner of the fens, I resorted to the bag of supplies that I had hurriedly assembled from the ruins of my hospital. I took a potent cocktail of antibiotics and waited. I quickly recovered. Though I sensed it was dangerous for me to do so, my conscience forced me to help others, too; several of whom were desperately ill but who ended up surviving the illness. Soon, rumours were going around that there was a healer in our midst. Some of them perhaps guessed correctly that I was a doctor with a survival bag, but they called me a healer nonetheless. It was a title which I adopted for my own safety. I would slip my pills down people's throats virtually unnoticed, while simultaneously I would perform for them a little magic ceremony with a glass of water.

'In little time, I acquired a reputation that spread around several villages. The afflicted would gather at my door, demanding to be healed. I did what I could, but the antibiotics could only last so long. As my supplies dwindled, I resorted to the other drugs I had salvaged from the hospital: not always cures, but an escape from wretched diseases for which people were no longer able to get any other treatment. In particular, I began to administer opiates. And how my reputation soared! I, the despised doctor who had had to run for my life, reinvented myself as that demon of late industrial society, a drug dealer. Wretches with anything from toothache to cancer would apply to my door for their chance to enter oblivion.

It had a sharp effect on the village in which I was living. Within weeks, dilated eyeballs had become the norm. The pangs of fear and hunger which governed many people at this time were greatly alleviated. Of course, I wondered at the morality of what I was doing, but my survival instinct was taking over from the high-mindedness which I had been taught at medical school. In return for my heroin I was guaranteed a full belly: people would turn up for their fix proffering chickens or young pigs as payment.

'Of course, my supplies of heroin could not last forever. But with the fields no longer cultivated to mechanical precision, the country grew thick with poppies: and so it became possible to manufacture an alternative. My kitchen I turned into an opium production line. I carried on happily in this way for some years, enjoying a sense of power in excess of that I had felt as a doctor in the industrial age. They were charmed times, in many ways, the first years after the collapse of industrialisation. Though terrible things were happening in the cities, it was possible to find backwaters where, as life became increasingly insular, it was possible to prosper. Many villages had become inhabited during the industrial age by quite learned folk. Those who had survived the plague found themselves in an environment which, although devoid of the luxuries which they had been used to, was in some ways attractive. In places there was a brief recovery of culture and learning. Books were still much read, music still played and sung. Fields were still being cultivated, and a certain amount of machinery and fuel still remained. Save for the times when illness struck, the immediate post-industrial age had the air of an Indian summer. The opium, of course, helped enormously.

'Yet there were emerging tensions which would bring us Progressive rule. It was remarkable the speed at which villages were diverging from each other, economically and socially. Deprived of the moderating influence of television, communities started to develop their own accents and dialects, and even to develop specific physical characteristics which set them apart from neighbouring communities. There was just a mile and a half between my village and the next, yet already mine was beginning to drop its 'aitches and the other one wasn't. While mine began to drink goats' milk and grew fat upon it, the other became largely vegetarian and flatulent. It was peculiar how differences emerged. My village took up goat-herding simply because there happened to be a family who, long before industrial society began to crumble, had bred a few goats as a hobby. From this small pool, large numbers of animals were bred, and the animals quickly became a staple of our diet.

'It wasn't so much hatred at this stage, but there began to emerge a deep suspicion of those who did not share the same tongue and customs as oneself. It was quite unpredictable; differences did not so much emerge along the old racial lines. It was other things which explained the growing tribalism of the country: one village, which was dominated by old farming families, would sneer at another because its population was heavily populated by former commuters. You could tell the latter because their backs were bent from the hours they had spent curled up in unnatural positions on trains and in cars, and because their eyes were poor.

'Dislikes turned to hatreds when rural areas were invaded by refugees from the towns: the urbanites as they came to be called. There were large numbers of people fleeing from the cities in search of safety, food, opportunity, and it was considered that these people threatened those of us who had already established ourselves a comfortable subsistence in the countryside. When an encampment appeared on a nearby hill we armed ourselves with sticks and drove out the invaders. Rarely after that was the word "urbanite" spoken without the speaker spitting in disgust.

'I would probably still have been living in that village had it not been struck by a collective fit of madness. Quite unexpectedly I was called before the parish council. I had made the mistake of travelling too often to other villages. A charge of practising medicine read before me. In spite of testimonies from several villagers that I was respected healer, the parish councillors seized my belongings and they found damning evidence: several white pills in the bottom of my medicine bag.

'I was sentenced to what they described as a warning: to be stretched. A rope was tied around my shoulders, another around my feet, and subjected to a tug 'o war. Three tugs I withstood, then screaming, I was let go. After two nights in great pain, I stole off, into the fen. For some months I continued to sell my opium, but it became harder to do so as more and more people had discovered the drug for themselves. A roughened tea made from poppies has become part of the diet. Medicine has gone back to its beginnings.

'My livelihood destroyed, I found my way to Cambridge and hammered on the door of Trinity College. As you remember, you offered me sanctuary, and I am grateful for that. There are too few refuges these days for the educated.'

7

We had not intended to take the main road to Royston, but so consumed were we by Olga's revelations that we lost track of the route we had intended to take through the back country. After some meandering we met the road that the industrial age knew dispassionately as the A10. It was a relief to come upon tarmac. The fields we had crossed had become an oppressive scrubland. The heavy clay lands of the south-east are now some of the most impenetrable stretches of country in England. If you wish to travel and yet to avoid the main roads, it has become necessary to head for the higher ground. The easiest land lies in the some of the places previously thought the most inhospitable: the moorlands of the north and west, where the soil is thin and the vegetation light. If you are in the south-east, you head for the chalk escarpments, for they remain quite bare. If you try to cross the clay, on the other hand, the chances are that you will start following an old track only to find it petering out in the thicket. Much of the day can be spent backtracking as you try in vain to find your way through.

Along parts of our route, the weeds had been beaten down by the wind and rain, but in others they grew up to our necks and beyond. We each took it in turns to take the lead, clearing the way with arms and fists through the prickly mass of vegetation: thistles, nettles and the odd clump of mangy wheat. In a few weeks' time these fields would become completely impassable: travel is now impossible in some places in high summer without a scythe. Thanks to this, the scythe has become a symbol for travel; in villages where Progressive rule is less well-established, it is hung outside inns as a means of advertising their presence to wayfarers. So much do weeds impinge upon our consciousness, that when people ask you about your journey, an account of the weeds which you met along your way invariably forms part of your reply. No longer is the word 'weed' synonymous with weakness: to call a person a weed these days is to accuse them of being a bully. Many stories are told of the weeds. It is held by those of Progressive persuasion that they are punishment for the farming practices of the industrial age. They are said to be the results of genetic experiments which went wrong, just as environmentalists in the late industrial age warned they would. It is impossible to say whether there is any truth in this theory, because we no longer have the means to tell whether any particular crop of weeds possesses genes introduced by Man. There are parts of the country which have been abandoned because of rumours that mutant plants are growing there, plants which are capable of entangling a man and killing him. People blame the genetic engineers of the industrial age for any form of plant-life which they find inconvenient or unpleasant. Ordinary nettles are widely believed to be tea plants which were deliberately manipulated by scientists, their sting having been introduced in order to deter trespassers from entering the fields where they grew. Similarly, poisonous species of toadstool are suspected of having been engineered to poison the poor who gather their food from the wild.

In the absence of science, people are free to believe whatever they like. Ordinary people receive many of their ideas through pronouncements made by a class of people known as the 'experts', usually employed by Progressive authorities. Do not be fooled: an expert is closer to what half a century ago would have been known as a PR officer. His expertise is solely in fooling the people. Many experts, I am sorry to say, are former academics who have opted for an easy life doing dirty work for the Progressives.

Even the main Royston road is much encroached upon by the undergrowth; in places it has halved in width; in others the tarmac is broken as roots have begun to break through the surface. But it will be some time before this sort of road becomes useless. Apart from suffering lacerations from one or two overhanging bramble bushes, we made easy progress, passing through a place called Harston, which was deserted save for a local man on a skateboard who looked upon us with some suspicion. We had travelled two more miles towards Foxton without incident, when, without warning, we encountered grave danger.

It was Bump who spotted the warning signs. On a drain cover beside the road sat a late middle-aged man, dressed in a torn leather jacket and tightly clutching a bottle. He was staring into space as we approached; then, catching sight of us, he leapt to his feet, shouted at us and threw the bottle at us. Fortunately, as he threw it, he seemed to lose his balance and it missed by some margin.

'Off with you!' he shouted. 'You have no business here.' Then his eyes glazed over and he became incapable of saying anything. We passed quickly on, but soon came upon several other similarly-aged inebriates, some of them lying on damp mattresses by the side of the road staring listlessly at the sky, some of them loitering in the middle of the road with wild staring eyes. We soon spotted the focal point of this strange community: an old petrol station around which perhaps fifty people had encamped. Many were sat around the pumps, sniffing from rags which from time to time they soaked in a clear, pungent liquid from bottles. Pervading all was a strong smell of petrol.

We tried to mind our own business, but several of the inebriates got to their feet and charged at us. Soon we were surrounded. More bottles were thrown, causing several of us to receive cuts from broken glass. We would quite likely have been killed had it not been for some quick thinking on the part of Dr Hoeffel. It was his practice always to carry with him an old cigar-lighter. He fumbled for it in his pocket, before seizing a bottle from one of the inebriates. He tore a strip from his shirt, stuffed it in the petrol-filled bottle and threw it in the crowd. As a fireball engulfed them, we ran, and kept on running for hundreds of yards.

In the next village, we learned the full story from an elderly man sat at the side of the road. Most petrol stations at the end of the industrial age had run dry of petrol. You can tell an old petrol station a mile before you come upon it because of the queues of rusting cars which lead towards it, they having been abandoned when supplies ran out. But there were a few petrol stations which, like the one at Foxton, had for obscure reasons never quite run dry. In the absence of their preferred drugs, locals began to inhale the last pungent gallons. The word got out and people travelled from miles around to sniff the petrol at Foxton. At first they would siphon it into cans and take it away, but as time went on addicts settled at Foxton and turned it into a kind of lowlife spa.

The phenomenon of petrol-sniffing amused Abdul greatly. 'I see that your civilisation has not lost its taste for oil,' he said. 'It always was a fatal addiction of yours.'

'But are you in the Islamic Empire not also users of oil?'

'We were back in the old days. But the use of oil has declined considerably since the religious wars, when supplies to the Christian world were quite deliberately cut off. There was great joy when the taps were turned off. We felt we were being freed from economic enslavement. Many of the wells were set alight in celebration. The land became lit by a chain of a thousand beacons from Egypt to Iran. So thick was the smoke that the sky went dark for weeks. This is greatly remembered in our culture. We turned our backs on oil and changed out habits totally.'

'You mean that you no longer have motor-cars?'

'There is great interest in motor-cars, and people do own them. But they would not dare drive them: they are too valuable. They are kept, and traded, as relics. Most work is now done by human hand or by animal.'

'What, then, has happened to the oil?' asked Alferris.

'It is sitting in the ground,' said Abdul, 'apart from small amounts which are used for heating homes in winter. But the production is on a small scale. And we certainly do not inhale it for pleasure.'

No-one was more affected by the sight of the petrol-sniffers than Bump. It was a disgrace, he said. He had thought such scenes of decadence were confined to the cities: that a community of petrol-sniffers should be living a few miles from Cambridge merely showed how far western society still had to progress. 'What idiocy in our midst!' he exclaimed. 'It must be swept away.' Bump was to have his way: later in our journey we were to learn that Progressive forces had entered Foxton and murdered every single one of the inebriates before setting the petrol station alight.

We came upon Royston as one comes upon many towns these days. About a mile from the first houses, the scrub began to give way to grassland as we reached the zone upon which the townspeople rely for their food. I will not call it farmland, because that implies a degree of ordered cultivation. Most communities no longer vest great effort in preparing land and planting crops; rather they have become scavenging societies. When the people of Royston set out to begin their harvest, they do not go to cut down neat rows of plants which they sowed months before; they go to a scrappy grassland dotted with potatoes and turnips, the descendants of plants left to run wild at the end of the industrial age. They gather what they need, then leave the plants to regenerate naturally. Many villages and small towns find it possible to meet all their needs in this way. The only contribution they make towards managing the land is in trampling down the young trees which would otherwise grow and choke the crops. The business of ploughing and tilling is now considered in some areas – particularly East Anglia – to be a blasphemy. There is a name for the industrial-scale farming of fifty years ago: 'rape', a word which has acquired more agricultural connotations than sexual ones. To leave the land alone, merely collecting its fruits as and when you need them, is regarded as more in keeping with nature and therefore with God's wishes. The passages of the Bible which refer to cultivation have fallen into disuse.

The reluctance to interfere with nature applies also to animals. Beasts are no longer domesticated; they are hunted in the wild by bands of men armed with long knives. After several hours in the bush, the hunters return to town pushing wheelbarrows full of dead chickens, or driving live pigs before them. Besides pigs and chickens, the countryside abounds with feral cows, goats and horses. Sheep, however, have all but died out. They have not been entirely forgotten, though: they have become semi-mythical beasts. People see photographs of a ram with long curly horns and fancifully imagine it to have been a noble beast which was driven to extinction by being hunted by man. The truth is more mundane: industrial age sheep were bred to grow fleeces so thick that, in the absence of regular shearing, it became impossible for a ram to gain entry to a ewe.

Sometimes, when men go out to hunt feral beasts, there are few to be found. But people would rather go hungry rather than take to domesticating animals. There is a fervour against keeping animals in captivity. To maltreat an animal, it is asserted, is to tempt seven years' famine. It is deemed wrong to put a beast in a cage or even to tether it. Awful tales are told of battery farming in the industrial era, when, it is widely believed, animals were implanted with mechanical systems and run on electricity. Industrial age animals, it is frequently claimed, especially in morality tales read to young children, went mad as a result of their treatment and sought their revenge. They turned their flesh to poison, killing millions. Never again, it is vowed, will humans interfere with the instincts and behaviour of animals. A moral code is strictly enforced. In Royston last winter, we were told, a woman was discovered feeding a chicken in a cage: a crime for which she was savagely beaten. Yet the strictures against the capture of animals do not extend to a prohibition against cruelty to wild animals, which are butchered in the most bloody manner. In this respect, the sensibilities of animal-lovers of the late industrial period have vanished. Animals are slaughtered with knives and axes in the street, before cheering crowds. Blood and entrails are a common sight on the tarmac.

The brutality could hardly be ignored as we entered the market square at Royston. Three youths were leading a hysterical pig to a stall. They kicked and whipped the animal, its squeals merely encouraging them. Then they slit the pig's throat, sending pulses of blood flowing into the gutters. The boys picked up the animal by its hind legs and hauled it along the street for a hundred yards or so in order to show off their kill. Finally, they put it down, and with the beast's face slumped on the tarmac, they began hacking at its body and selling its meat and offal. An enthusiastic crowd gathered, while across the street several elderly people cried at the savagery of it all. At first, their protests were dismissed as the ramblings of madmen. Then a member of the crowd shouted at them 'Vegetarians!' Several dozen joined in the chanting, waving knives at the elderly onlookers until they were driven away. Vegetarianism, though a popular creed at the end of the industrial age, has been denounced in recent years as an unnatural practice.

Once the pig had been dissected and sold, the centre of Royston returned to slumber. Business is still done in shops, but trade in manufactured goods is slow. You do not make a living from selling the likes of steel saucepans and wooden spoons: they are so much in abundance that they are virtually given away. Shops are sepulchral places; they contain row upon row of manufactures, entombed in dust beneath long-faded signs with messages like 'final clearance sale' and '2 for the price of 1'. Should you wish to buy an item, it is often necessary to go searching down the street to find the shopkeeper. It is rarely thought necessary for shopkeepers to guard their premises against theft: the goods are worth so little, and in any case thieves are easily apprehended in the insular societies in which people now live.

We looked for an inn, but we were told that none in Royston remained. We were directed instead to an old bed shop. The owner, it turned out, had long since despaired of selling his wares and had taken instead to the business of putting travellers up for the night. His was a strange hostel, a corrugated steel shed near the old bypass, laid out with rows of beds still covered in the polythene sheeting in which they had been wrapped decades before. The shopkeeper, a bright-eyed man in his 70s with warty hands at which he kept picking, said that people occasionally came in to buy sheets and pillows – especially after outbreaks of plague – and that from this he made a meagre living. But it was a dozen years since he had sold his last bed. And yet, so typically among elderly businessmen, he refused to believe that all was lost.

'This recession,' he said as he led us to our beds, 'it cannot last much longer, can it? Things must pick up, mustn't they? Every spring I say this to myself: the weather is getting better, so maybe it will tempt buyers to the shops once again. It is a foul recession, this one, to be sure. But even when I started my career in retailing, when the aisles of this shop could not cope with the numbers of shoppers waving their credit cards, business was always up and down. That's what people forget. We had to keep doing special offers to get people in through the doors, even in those days. Perhaps I shall have another of my sales this summer and business will be back to something approaching where it started.'

The bed shop-owner was foolish in his hopes, but he was far from alone in harbouring fanciful ideas about economic recovery. Even now, there are people who cling onto share certificates in the belief that one day they will recover in value. Some people in the country have plans to make dangerous visits to London, in order to seek out dealers in stocks and shares. They know of others who have gone to London in order to do this. The fact that these people often fail to return is sometimes taken as a positive sign – why, if John has not come back, they tell themselves, it must be because he has sold his shares and is living the high life on the proceeds!

There is no prospect at all that retail business will return to levels seen in the industrial age, but there is some comfort to be gained from imagining that it can. We spent all evening reminiscing with the shopkeeper about the good old days when he was selling several dozen beds a week. As we spoke, his optimism turned slowly to anger.

'They really knew about shopping in those days, they did,' he said. 'There's no-one who knows about credit agreements any more, no-one who cares about quality. When people see something these days, they say "oh, that'll do". What kind of an empty life is that? It's all spiritualism, these days, isn't it. Never mind trying to achieve anything in this world, just look forward to the next one: that's what they seem to think. It's a lazy way of thinking, a cop-out. They have no pride in their acquisitions at all. I could go on, but it's only making me angry.'

The shopkeeper intrigued Alferris, who had much to say. 'But there were people back in the industrial age who used to say much the same thing about materialism: that it was empty, that it was too easy an option. That it required no faith.'

'Too easy an option!' said the shopkeeper. 'Do you know the hours I used to put in, the effort it took to become a regional sales manager? Harder than a life of prayer, if you ask me.'

'But it required no faith.'

'No faith! What about faith in this?' asked the shopkeeper as he took out a credit card and bent it between forefinger and thumb. To believe in a currency which consisted of nothing more than little pulses of electricity flashing between the world's computers: that's faith. That's true faith. Oh, I remember the tirades against materialism, to be sure. But who in his heart can really admire the wretched monk on his wooden stool more than the tycoon in his helicopter? People have lapsed into spiritualism, if you ask me, because it is an easier option to the mental work and physical effort which used to go into acquiring possessions.'

Our host had much to get off his chest. He had been long in the retail trade, and spoke in wonderment of things which mean nothing to most people now. 'Just look at this sofa,' he gestured. 'I could pull it apart and break it down to its original pieces. And do you know what I could show you? That they came from all over the world. Screws from Taiwan, foam from Malaysia, cloth from China, and the lot shipped to Britain to be assembled. The beauty of it! It was the same with any manufactured goods, and the same with food. Ah, the supply chains: they were true works of genius! So very different from the lazy eating of today when people just pick their food from the nearest bush, having never tasted food from outside their neighbourhood.'

Most of my party, I have to say, were unmoved. It is an uphill struggle trying to impress upon people today such things as the science of goods distribution. Knowledge is dying by the day because of the difficulty of conveying it to the next generation. The scholar has so much he wishes to tell and so few people wanting to understand. Abdul took much down, but it is almost certain that he was able to make little of it afterwards. The study of history was a much more pleasing business in your day, when it was a process of discovery. Now it is a business of salvage, conducted by a few people who feel compelled to keep alive what they can of the great age just past. In the past historians used to flatter themselves that they were gradually uncovering truths, that the understanding of an age improved the further that age receded into the past. It is no longer possible to think like this. It is obvious that knowledge and understanding of the industrial age is declining rapidly. The business of teaching in the present age is like having half an hour to save books from a library beset by rising tidewaters: it is a case of deciding what you most wish to save, and just accept you will have to miss the rest. The logistics of supply chains in the industrial age is one of the subjects I fear will be allowed to go.

The audience of an historian these days is a very small number of young scholars. These are usually the children of older scholars. Occasionally, however, I have been approached by independent-minded young people who somehow have managed to develop an interest in our industrial past in spite of the hostility of their parents and their peers. As for the majority of people, even simple tales fail to impress them nowadays. You might imagine post-industrial folk would be interested in stories of fast cars, aeroplanes, computers and other machinery. But it is not the case. On the few occasions I have dared enter a tavern in recent years – not to be recommended, for these have become places of vice as never before – I have invariably encountered a young man yawning at, sneering at, treating with contempt an elder boasting of how fast-paced his life used to be. There is no quicker way to lose a young person's attention than to start to tell him: 'when I was young, it used to be possible to fly from London to New York and back – all in a day'. Such things are so totally at odds with the young person's experience that they are beyond his comprehension, and he merely stares into his beer and mutters 'what for?'

It is far from uncommon to meet people who, like the shopkeeper in Royston, attempt to carry on with life as if nothing had happened in the past 50 years. Older people engage in all kinds of obsessive behaviour connected with their previous life. There is one man in Cambridge who still rises at 6:30 every morning, dons a business suit and walks to his former office where he will spend all his day reading yellowed documents drawn from filing cabinets: he cannot bring himself to admit that his business no longer exists. Another fellow spends most of his days cleaning and polishing his car and telling anybody who will listen how fast it will go and how many miles to the gallon it will do, seemingly convinced that he will once again have a chance to drive it. There is a lady across the road from Trinity College who is to be seen several times a day talking into a telephone: it must be to herself, for nobody else will be able to hear her.

But there are more extreme cases than this. Beyond the bounds of the remaining towns and villages lives a race of backwoodsmen who retreated to the hills when industrial civilisation faded and are completely ignorant of what has happened in the intervening years. They are hardy, scavenging types who trap birds and collect nuts and berries; intelligent people who quickly became adept at survival techniques and who ever since have avoided the risk of seeking human company. They are so wrapped up in their life of self-sufficiency that they have no wish to emerge from the bush to see what has happened to the rest of humanity. What they do not know, they make up. They are the last proponents of industrial age individualism: they still believe that mankind is best served when every man pursues his own dream; even when that dream is limited to snaring rabbits and extracting water from muddy springs. They guard their privacy so well that it can be dangerous to cross paths with them.

We encountered one of these feral beings the following day on our way from Royston. We emerged into a clearing to see before us a hovel lashed together from branches and old scraps of corrugated iron and plastic fertilizer bags. From a washing line hung a tattered shirt, while in the foreground was a burned patch of grass scattered with bones. Our first instinct was to retreat: fearing the presence of a putrid human corpse. Then, as we approached, we must have tripped an invisible alarm system, because there came from the hovel the sound of a ringing bell. Out came a wild-eyed creature, the cartoon image of a hermit, except that instead of wearing a beard down to his toes he was clean-shaven. To continue to shave every morning, he was to explain, was a matter of pride; though he had to pay for his meticulousness with a blotched and bloody chin: he had been using the same – disposable – razor for what he estimated to be 20 years. His clothes had withstood time well, a tribute to the quality of his tailoring. Yet they served to make him a peculiar sight: he was wearing what was instantly recognisable as a business suit.

He was brandishing a knife when he emerged from his hovel, and it was only after some time that we managed to persuade him not to use it. We did not mean to disturb him, we explained, but we had lost our way. Could he direct us to Baldock? He seemed surprised by the question, as if he did not realise that he was near that town. His voice was staccato, whiny – unused – though he gradually became more fluent. He could not seem to decide whether to be friendly or angry, but settled for something in between.

'Back, back,' he said. 'Come any closer and I will kill you all. Can you not see this is my place?'

'I am sorry that we have disturbed you,' I said. 'But it is so difficult to keep to the tracks any more. We are lost. We wish only to pass. We have a long journey ahead, to London.'

The creature stared at us for some time, palpitating and perspiring. The sense of hostility was profound. 'Nobody goes to London any more. It is not there. Nobody can get close to the place where that city once stood: it is a burned hole in the ground. The few who remain in this country have taken to the woods, like me. But you should keep your distance. There is nothing here for you. I have trapped the birds for several hundred yards around, and they are mine. Why do you come to disturb me? I have not seen human life for a long time. Not since the year of the aphids. It is just the wild dogs I have a problem with. They are quite vicious.' He showed us a long scar in his wrist. 'This happened a while back. I was left for dead. I was only saved because the animal was still wearing its former owner's chain. With this I managed to choke the beast. It is good that I took the trouble to learn these skills. Most people didn't; that is why they have all died. People, no I haven't seen any of them since the time of the aphids. How did you get here, and what do you want?'

In time we managed to convince him that we meant no harm. Though he never put his knife down all the time that we were with him, and he was to wave it at us several times completely unprovoked, he became expansive; as if, much to his surprise, he suddenly found himself enjoying human company. Putting together his broken speech, he introduced himself something like this:

'I can't tell you how long I've been here. After my watch batteries went flat in the year 2043, I used to keep several sticks beside my bed in which I cut notches. I did this for about three years, then I lost my sticks and lost count. It has been some years, though, since I set up home here. I started in Norfolk, in Thetford Forest, but I wandered around a lot in the early years, to the point that I lost my bearings and I am no longer sure where I am. It is unhealthy, living in the same place. But keep moving onto fresh ground and you can avoid contaminating your water supply with your own excrement. This way you also avoid the bandits. This is how I survived the war. It is a good job I left London: the city was flattened and burned. The smoke reached as far as here, and I suppose I am 100 miles from where London used to be. Once, I walked southwards for two days and I came into a clearing of burnt undergrowth. That is the edge of the destruction that was wrought on London: beyond that there is no life at all. Soon after the war, there was a winter harsher than any I can remember. If I was counting the days correctly, the snow must have lain into June. The woods were frozen and dead. There was only one way to find food, and that was to dig, dig and dig. The frosts were so hard, the first foot or so of soil was frozen, but once you got below that, you came to the worms. Have you eaten worms? You must have eaten them, for you have been through the same harsh times as I have. They are good food, once you can get over your disgust. When I couldn't find worms, I was reduced to gnawing at my shoes for comfort. It was a nuclear winter: just like they said it was going to be.'

I could not let this pass. 'A nuclear winter? There has been no nuclear winter.'

The feral creature came close to me, and held his knife up to my chin. 'Are you trying to tell me that there has been no nuclear war? But I saw it with my own two eyes, heard it with my own two ears. There were flashes to the south-east, like lightning, though of a more brilliant orange. And thick clouds, especially thick at the top: mushroom-shaped, just like in the books. The next day, the rain burned my skin. I heard cries: that was the people dying. I fell ill. For months I was constantly dizzy. I still have scars on my back. I wandered around in a daze, though I recovered. I saw no people for months afterwards. Then came the winter. You cannot tell me there was no nuclear war.'

'You have imagined it. There was no nuclear war. There were many people who believed the civilised world would end with atomic warfare, and there were times when it seemed this was inevitable. But the war never came.'

The fingers of the feral creature tightened upon the handle of his knife.

'What, then, happened to the bombs? These weapons cannot simply have disappeared. That is improbable. They must have fallen into the wrong hands. And once that happened, they must have been exploded. It couldn't have been any other way. It would have been too much of a temptation not to use these weapons. War is in our blood.'

'That may be true, but I assure you the weapons were not used. It is a puzzle why they were not used during the latter stages of the industrial age, especially during the religious wars, when nuclear war was widely expected. But any bombs which fell into the hands of warlords and rogues were immediately rendered useless.

They needed great expertise to detonate and they were very quick to decay. They are still guarded, mind you, or at least they were half a dozen or so years back, when I last passed Lakenheath, one of the military bases where they used to be kept. I saw guardsmen defending them, marching before the bunkers with great pomp. They answer to no higher authority any more, these guardsmen, but still they continue their duty because it is all they know. There are people who still claim to possess the means to wage nuclear warfare, but it is all talk. These bombs cannot be remade, for they require much more precision than contemporary minds possess. Once in a tavern I came across a Progressive with a plan for obliterating the City of London. He was going to set off a nuclear bomb, he said, and with it would be destroyed the final shreds of global capitalism. This would be the last-ever bomb, he said. It would not be permissible to make bombs in the future, though the destruction of counter-revolutionary industrialists would be justified. I found him fearsome until he showed me the drawings of the device which he intended to deploy. I took one glance and saw the axe with which he was intending to split his atom and I knew I need listen to this fool no longer. There are people who can recall some of the terminology of nuclear science, but it has been reduced to myth.'

By now, the feral creature was becoming quite agitated. Still holding his knife, he retreated a little way to his tent. He felt around inside and withdrew a shotgun. My fellow travellers were shocked, and several turned to run. But it was quite unnecessary: I correctly guessed that the feral creature had exhausted all his ammunition while hunting years before. 'Stand at least ten yards from me,' he said. 'Back, all of you, behind that tree. I don't know what you want. I can't trust you. But was there ever a time when you could sleep safely in your bed? Like hell, was there. The years of so-called "civilisation" were the worst of the lot. I lived in a cell, sealed from the outside world behind large gates: a luxury apartment, they called it at the time. I had video entry phones and infra-red cameras. My car, I hard to park in a secure compound. I used to be able to get from my flat to my car, then drive out onto the motorways without once having to draw breath from the outside air. It was a completely unnatural life. But if you were wealthy you dared do any different in the cities of the industrial age: they were populated by thugs who would kill you for your watch.

'Do you know what used to be meant by "civilisation"? I'm sure I don't. The word seemed to suggest that we had stopped being driven by our bestial urges and instead had become motivated by art, music, poetry: all the nice things. It was a charming conceit, but the more one looked behind the veneer of civilisation, the more one saw the wormwood: the lusts, the passions, the violence. Even artists preyed upon their rivals – a gruesome world, it was, art. And as for those of us in business, we hardly bothered to put up the pretence of being part of this mythical civilisation. Deep inside my double-breasted suit there was the heart of a primate. I was a management consultant. It was my job to teach businesses that they were ruled by the law of the jungle.

'When we were training, we used to head for the hills for exercises in bonding and survival. We played war games, firing little balls of paint at each other. We climbed, canoed, anything that involved getting cold, muddy and having to survive. Sometimes, the idea was that we learned how to trust people; sometimes it was to build our self-confidence. But I think there was something a bit deeper than that. We were living out a little fantasy: surviving as if we were the last people on Earth. One weekend we were dropped by helicopter somewhere in the Scottish Highlands. We had a bit of food, a little tent and some survival clothing. The idea was to camp overnight, then find our way back to a base. I did okay. I survived and managed all that was demanded of me. But something clicked inside me, that weekend, while I was setting up my tent on those moors. I thought: what if it really comes to this? What if some years from now mankind is reduced to this? What if we reverted from living in an urban jungle to living in a real one? What if there was no warm office to go back to on a Monday morning? How would we really get on?

'The more I thought about it, the more attractive the idea became. There was great dissatisfaction with the industrial way of life, even among the successful. Making money engaged us for a while; but sooner or later we would look down at our atrophied bodies and feel disgust. Our minds were stretched, but our muscles? They never came properly to be used. A man could live his life physically unchallenged. Manual work had disappeared, been superseded by worthless jobs which turned men into shadows of their forefathers. The industrial system was a great achievement, but it left us with a problem: we had made ourselves redundant, designed ourselves out of the system. So this was why we took to the Scottish hills: to force ourselves to be human, to regain our manhood.

'It was a short step, I guess, from play-acting to starting to wish you were doing it for real. Fifty years ago I think there were a lot of people like me, who secretly wanted to see an end to the industrialised world. We were too comfortable, too wealthy. We treated our possessions with disdain: our cars were mere playthings, to be used, abused and then dumped for a newer model. One day I found myself watching the screens in a bank where I was working. The economic news was bad, very bad. I should have been grimacing, thinking of the jobs which would be lost, of the dreams wasted, of the hardship which lay ahead. Yet, strangely I didn't feel any of these things. No, I found myself willing the economy to collapse. I wanted the chaos, I wanted the warfare because I wanted to be forced to live, not just be carried along on some conveyor belt to a pampered old age and death. I don't think I was the only one who felt this way. In fact, I know I wasn't. I studied the people around me, and I could see in their faces a feeling of contented resignation that the game was almost up.

'Quickly I moved from willing the end of economic system to making actual preparations for it. Like many of those in my position, I started to buy land. I wanted to know that I had the means to feed myself when the great crash came. I learned the rudiments of animal husbandry and I bought shotguns so that I might be able to defend myself against the hungry masses who inevitably would be set loose upon the land. I wasn't alone: there were many of us consultants, bankers, businessmen who went overnight from a life of computers and air-conditioning to one of roughened subsistence. My neighbours could not understand me. They could not come to terms with wealthy, successful people like me who descended amongst them, hankering after a simple life. The rural people of the industrial age would sell you a field of productive soil for the price of a holiday in Spain and think they had done well out of the bargain. They were in no position to understand how fragile, how illusory were the principal assets of industrialisation: the shares, the bonds, the paper promises which were to vanish so quickly. Nothing in life has given me such pleasure as observing the days of economic meltdown from the safety of my little estate in Norfolk.

'For a couple of years I lived off my land, tilling the soil, making bread. It seemed so clever, to have picked such a secluded spot so far away from the turmoil then running through the cities. Then the refugee raids happened. I suppose I should have seen them coming. Without law and order, the titles to land became just as worthless as the shares. With a gun you can defend yourself against one man at a time, maybe two, maybe three. But against the gangs of starving refugees which swept across Norfolk, pillaging and raping the countryside? I killed three or four of these refugees, but to what purpose? I knew their families would come back within hours to finish me off. So I packed a small bag and spent the night in the forest. In the morning, from a distance, I watched my house explode in a fireball. Fuel, I guess, had been spread through the house and then set alight. That's what happened to the last petrol supplies in the countryside: they were expended in an orgy of burning.

'From then on, I kept moving. It was the safest thing to do. I loved my estate, but I have come to prefer the peripatetic life, wandering about, never sure where my supper is coming from and where I am going to shelter for the night. To many people at the time, brought up on central heating and fast food, it was beyond belief how people could survive out of doors, living off the fat of the land. But it is not hard to do this. It is just necessary first to remove from your mind the sensation of warmth and security. From there, all else follows. I am sure the survival instincts are in all of us; they have not been entirely snuffed out by soft living. Once you have got over the disgust of munching a cockroach, of skinning a rat, there is plenty of protein available in the woods.

'A lot of people died because they panicked. It was sad to see, but in the last 40 or 50 years of industrialisation, the physical resilience of the population collapsed. We ended up with a population which could recite the litany of foods implicated in the causation of cancer but which could not tell the difference between a mushroom which would nourish them and one which would poison them. Industrial peoples possessed great skill in managing their appearance to their social advantage, but they had not the first clue how to cut an abscess from the foot or to amputate a gangrenous finger. Amputation, you see, that's a skill I had to master early on. See this stump on my right hand? Blood poisoning, that's what I had. I didn't hang about: a obtained a flint, which I sterilised in flame, and chopped the finger straight off. It was a disgrace that people became so soft, so helpless when it came to simple operations like this. People who attempted to live wild were forced into houses with central heating and power showers. I remember how at the peak of the industrial age an elderly man was discovered living on a hillside in Wales. He had learned everything he needed to know: how to eat, how to build shelter, how to survive. Yet rather than earning praise, he was forced, against his will, to move into a flat. How cruel, and how wicked. No, I do not regret the passing of industrialisation. It was an oppressive system in how it attempted to suppress our instincts.

'Don't bother trying to tell me that it was a superior system because people were much healthier then and lived longer. They were only healthy as long as they had their chemicals and medicines to keep them alive. All the while, the genetic stock of mankind was declining. The trouble was that the weak were no longer being naturally culled, so that the genetic quality of mankind was diminishing. That's what the problem was. But now we have the chance to start again from scratch, you see. I know it caused great misery, the nuclear war which you refuse to believe happened, but ultimately it will have turned out to be an advantage to mankind. It has strengthened our stock: that's what it has done. When the population recovers, it will be stronger. Maybe it sounds cruel to say so, but ultimately that war will prove to have been a good business decision .'

8

We left the feral creature and continued on to Baldock, a journey
interrupted by a rainstorm which rumbled in from the west like a
foul mood. We were grateful, in the mist and confusion, for the
old road signs which, though bent and stained, still mark the way
to every town and village. It must be hard to imagine for you,
brought up in an age of drains and culverts – those under-
appreciated, barely-seen wonders – the terror which rain can now
bring. With much of the old drainage system blocked and broken,
swirling pools and torrents can appear after mild downpours. The
main roads, otherwise well preserved, are now dissected in places
by deep gullies filled with boulders and pasty clay where the
tarmac has been savagely eroded by a seasonal river. There are
many basins, dry land in your day, which remain in flood all
winter, becoming breeding grounds for malarial diseases. Few care
to live in these fenny wastes, preferring the higher, more
absorbent chalk lands. But many people come down to fish in the
seasonal lakes, setting out on makeshift rafts or in old, half-
perished rubber dinghies which all too often burst or capsize,
tipping their sailors to their deaths. It is common in spring, when
the water levels drop, to find the bodies of unfortunates who so
met their deaths, their bloated bodies entangled in weeds. On but

a few days of the winter do the river basins of England open up: during times of hard frost when it is possible to don a pair of old skates – one of the few contraptions of the industrial age which still fulfils it original purpose – and travel down frozen watercourses, experiencing a phenomenon which has otherwise disappeared from life: speed. The elderly are especially keen on skating, but the pleasures are by no means restricted to them. On these few icy days, the Progressives often drop their strictures against travel – ice skates being not in any sense mechanical – and the fit skate off twenty, thirty miles in a long-suppressed spirit of discovery. Youths take to the ice and skate off to challenge neighbouring villages to vast, unruly games of ice hockey which are as much tribal warfare as sport. Then the thaw sets in and the tedium and insularity of contemporary life returns.

It took us until evening to reach Baldock. When we did so we were but nine miles from Royston, but the mood of the two places could not have been more different. Where Royston had a feel of joyous anarchy about it, there was a severity to Baldock which became obvious as soon as we walked into the thickened highway that serves as the market square. There were few people about, but those whom we did chance upon took a scowling interest in us, peeping out from beneath the hoods of their shell suits and staring at us with an intensity and for a length of time which would have been considered indecent in the industrial age; now that crowds are a rarer phenomenon and interaction with strangers is less common, intense staring has become part of normal human intercourse.

Baldock, we were soon to learn, was firmly under Progressive rule. It was our good fortune, before the authorities could catch up with us, to come upon the address of a safe house which had been given to me by a wandering scholar some months before. The safe house turned out to be run by a group calling themselves the Knights Industrialists, who had set up the hostel in order to shelter educated people attempting to make the journey between

London and the old industrial cities of the north. It was an anonymous house in the late-industrial suburbs, embedded within a dense wood of 100 foot high conifers and surrounded by impenetrable thickets of pampas grass. There was no sign outside, and neighbouring properties appeared to be empty. We knocked three times then three times again, in accordance with the agreed code, and were let in by a bearded man by the name of Derek, the master of the house.

There was no-one else there that evening save for a young, studious Yorkshire girl called Sonia who had travelled down from the north disguised as a man, with a thick cloth cap drawn tightly over her head and her chin obscured with a scarf. Over a meal of fried cabbage and stinging, effervescent beer, she told us with great animation of the latest developments in her homeland.

'My journey has been hard. It is not wise to travel as a woman. I have been unable to wash since Newark, where my disguise was rumbled by a suspicious landlord who peeped into the bathroom while I was washing. Word went round quickly about "the woman from Yorkshire" and locals came to stare at the oddity of a woman travelling alone. I was violated several times by drunken louts. After this, I concealed myself in a cupboard and left in the early hours, travelling overnight across the fields and woods.

'But it has been good to travel. Where I live there are many people who have never been more than a couple of streets in any direction. I come from Leeds, I do, and oh, a very stubborn lot they are up there, for sure. They are so proud, and quite set in their ways. There is an uncomplicated friendliness to them, but one which does not allow for the possibility of there being anything for them to learn from the outside world – in spite of their obvious poverty.

'They know what they like and there is no shifting them from it: prayers like clockwork, three times a day, at one of the many mosques. An old-fashioned curry, washed down with a sickly sweet preparation of dried nettles they call tea. The men are insistent upon wearing beards. Any grown man with a clean-shaven chin is the object of much derision – he is called a "nancy", a word of obscure Islamic origin, I understand. The women cover their heads with old rags. It is an old custom, which some women find inconvenient and have begun to discard, to the disapproval of older folk. The men wear shawls and look painfully thin. They would be better fed if they would eat the wild pigs which scavenge in the old parks, but they will not touch them. It is said that this strange custom derives from pigs having been pumped full of chemicals during the industrial age to make them grow. Starved of protein, the faces of Leeds folk are pasty and white, for which outsiders mock them. My parents tell me there was a time when the muslim faith was synonymous with a dark skin. In a few muslims I can see what they mean, but it is certainly no longer generally the case.

'The streets of Leeds are a painful sight. Like so many of the towns of Yorkshire, Leeds has been torn apart by the religious wars. The muslims have driven the christians further and further into the suburbs, converting many christians and atheists as they go. It is not so much the finer points of theology which attract people to the muslim faith, but the prospect of little freedoms. For example, muslim women are not expected constantly to satisfy the urges of their husbands. Thirty years ago, it is said by older folk, terrible stories were told about the muslims, about how they would put to death those who did not share their faith, and how they would chop the hands from children who stole. I think their memories must be failing them, for it is with christians that these are things associated. Just last year, there was a hand-chopping at Keighley, which many attended from miles around, bringing picnics and beer. A good number of them had reserved the best vantage points days in advance. One christian scholar proudly showed me a drawing which he had made of the occasion: it showed crowds of church-going people cheering as the axe was brought down upon the wrists of an unfortunate youth – who had been caught stealing a loaf of bread. But was this not a muslim tradition, I asked, for I had been told it was? Not at all, said the scholar, quite offended: it was a christian one. And he showed me the evidence in the bible, which was compelling. The muslims, he said, were decadent, and cared little for the moral decay of their society.

'Many people who live on the fringes of northern cities think the same way. The easy ways of muslim society are renowned. For that reason, many atheists have chosen to settle in Leeds rather than in the surrounding country. In the outer districts of the city there is much trouble from christian gangs who make regular incursions into muslim areas armed with sticks and flaming torches of burning pig fat.

'Most christians have left, to the Pennines, to the Dales or to the Moors. The countryside was barbaric for some years, but there is governance of a kind re-emerging. A local tyrant has set up a fortress on the site of an ancient village called Wharram Percy, and taken the name Percy for himself. Quite a personality cult has built up around him. The village, so Percy's followers assert, is one of the few sites which remains pure, having been occupied in ancient history but having been abandoned during the industrial age. Percy is said to be a brave man, who is leading a crusade to seize the central mosque in York – or what the christians insist on calling the Minster. Attacks are frequent and vicious. There are many fewer muslims in York than in Leeds, and there is always the possibility of the former city falling to Percy's men. At one point it was said that Percy's forces were barely 100 metres from the mosque, though they have taken heavy casualties and it is far from certain that they can survive. Ultimately the muslims have the advantage in this struggle because they have petrol bombs. They have access to these weapons because the ways of the industrial age are so much more embedded in their culture. It is said that the cities of the north are full of underground petrol tanks.'

I looked at Alferris, who looked at Abdul, who looked at me. 'What do you mean by this, the industry is more embedded in the muslims' culture?' asked Alferris.

'I mean what I say,' said Sonia, 'that the muslims have their industrial past to draw upon. They have a long tradition of working with oil, and have have managed to preserve supplies of it, deep in the tanks of petrol stations in the city.'

'What do you mean, a long tradition of working with oil? Surely, the christian population have a longer tradition with industrial things.'

'Islam and industrialisation, they are one of the same thing,' said Sonia. 'The fringes of northern Europe were quiet, agrarian places until the muslims brought oil from the middle east and built up the cities.'

Abdul was unhappy. 'But this is absurd. It goes against everything I have learned. Industrialisation began in the christian world, long before there were large numbers of muslims living there. What is the basis for this strange belief?'

'It is clear,' said Sonia. 'If you look at a city like Leeds, the oldest mills lie in the muslim areas; it was there that the industrial age began, with the manufacture of white cotton garments: the sort of shawls still worn by the muslims. Christians have always been rural people: it is obvious, because that is where the churches are. The christians took up industrialisation only late in the industrial age; we know this because the christians live on the fringes of the cities, where the later factories and warehouses are to be found.'

'But you know, surely, of the migration of muslims to Britain during the industrial age?' asked Alferris.

'What migration?' asked Sonia. 'The muslims have always been in Leeds for as long as Leeds has been there.'

What could we say? It was a revelation to meet Sonia. She was so bright and seemingly so educated, yet her understanding of history extended back little further than her own lifetime. How quickly is history becoming blurred! Can anything be done, or is the past inevitably to be lost to myth? It was with a sense of disquiet that I stared into the remains of my fried cabbage.

At first light we continued our journey towards Stevenage where, we had been informed, a railway service had been reinstated to convey visitors the rest of the way to London. But before we left, there was grave news. A traveller, a learned man of some acquaintance from Cambridge, arrived at the safe house and demanded to see us. He had walked through the night. In Cambridge, we were being talked about as subversives. The day after we left, Trinity College had been raided and the scholars who remained there imprisoned at the Guildhall. The Master's Lodge had been burned. The rest of the college buildings had been put under guard, and had been promised to whoever managed to deliver my head to Cambridge. It was certain that there would be some Progressive thugs on our trail.

It would take us two hours, we reckoned, to reach Stevenage railway station by way of the main road. By the backroads it would be three. After some disagreement, we decided to take the main road in spite of the dangers which that entailed. Almost immediately we ran into suspicion: at a roundabout at the southern end of the town stood a sentry armed with a long wooden club. We considered trying to pass ourselves off as harmless peasants on our way to the fields, but decided not to chance it. Instead, we took a detour through an old car park dotted with burned-out vehicles. Beyond the car park was a long stone and glass building, where we took shelter. Almost immediately Alferris spotted where he was.

'It is astounding,' he said. 'To think that it was over 20 years ago that I last stood in this building. It was here that I began as a novice, shuffling up and down these aisles in my uniform, with my head bowed in awe of the place. How full the supermarkets were then! These aisles were full of serious-minded people pushing their trolleys, to the accompaniment of music wafting from high above. And look at it now: empty save for half a dozen elderly people who have set up stalls trying to sell tired old goods to other elderly folk. There is a feel of death, here.'

Alferris was quite right. The supermarket still performed some kind of economic function, but it was a pitiful one. All items of food had long since been removed, but there remained on the shelves a number of medications and toiletries. The ownership of this stock had been assumed by a class of traders who sat hopefully behind their stalls in the hope of attracting custom. No-one under 50 entered the supermarket while we were there, but half a dozen elderly ladies traipsed up and down, examining jars of moisturisers, bottles of deodorant and other industrial age comforts which have all but fallen into disuse. Tiny sums were asked for these goods, but even so the shoppers showed great reluctance to commit themselves to any purchase. One lady unscrewed several jars of face cream and in each case smothered a tiny amount on her cheeks, before finally buying one. Later, outside the shop, we saw her applying the cream to her face, to much derision from youths. 'Look at her!' said one. 'Her skin is like leather, but still she keeps rubbing in those poisons. She is making her face worse. When will these old people ever overcome their ignorance?'

The serious commerce was taking place outside the old supermarket, in a corner of the car park which had been designated as a 'farmers' market'. Several dozen traders were standing about with wire trolleys stuffed with food, mostly cabbages, parsnips, carrots and a bulbous root I took to be sugar beet. Several hundred townsfolk had turned out to see what was on offer. 'Ten carrots for a coin!' cried one of the traders. 'Any coin will do, so long as it has a head on the back.' Another cried: 'Best sugar beet, pulled fresh this morning! Eat or ferment into spirit!' Most of the goods, it transpired, had been scavenged from fields close to the town. Three or four men, bearing distinctive caps dyed with what looked like beetroot juice, went about the wire trolleys trying to determine the origin of the goods. These inspectors, we learned, were employed by the Lord of the Manor to ensure the quality of the food on sale. They sniffed it, carefully examined the dirt clinging to it and asked the traders questions as to where they had found it.

Most of the roots were caked in a thick, chalky clay. But one trolley-load of carrots was covered with a drier, sandier dust. It caught the inspectors' attention at once. They prodded the carrots, rubbed the dust between their fingers and asked the alarmed trader: 'where did these come from?' The trader bit his lip and muttered: 'north end of the town, by the old motorway'. One of the inspectors then broke a carrot in half and put the broken end of the root to his tongue. 'This is not Baldock food!' he then declared. 'This is foreign muck! I order you to tell me where it came from.' At some length, the trader then admitted that he had collected the carrots from fields to the north of Biggleswade two days before. At this point, other traders had gathered around his trolley. To much shouting, and with the tacit approval of the inspectors, they overturned the trolley and stamped upon the carrots. The poor trader turned and ran. 'Off with you!' one of the inspectors then shouted, breaking open one of the carrots and pressing into its flesh with his fingernails. 'This food is not safe! Look at it! It has become globulised.'

The globules to which he was pointing were imaginary. The word 'globulisation', used these days to describe the process of degradation which food is believed to undergo when it is moved more than a few miles, is clearly a corruption of 'globalisation'. But few understand this, and so go on believing that non-locally grown food is full of poisonous globules. It is so typical of the misconceptions which arise nowadays.

My party lunched frugally and then found our way out of the car park onto a back road. We were quickly on our way towards Stevenage, via a long route. As soon as were clear of the town, I asked Alferris to tell us more of his career in the supermarket.

'I spent several months here as a novice, but it became rapidly clear that there was no future in becoming a supermarket manager and so I left,' he said. 'I made a decision that many were making at the time: to join the church. We could see the way things were going. The church did not offer the same sense of fulfilment as did working in commerce, but at least it offered a secure future.

'It is far from straightforward to explain why the masses turned sharply away from secularism and back to religion. In the latter years of the industrial age the churches appeared to be dying. Congregations in many places were down to half a dozen elderly souls. Churches were closing. The practice of public worship became little more than an act of pageantry. Religious folk had been reduced to comic turns. Monks, vicars, bishops; all became figures of fun. We considered the spiritual life to be an absurdity.

'At the time, many people believed it would not be long before religious observance died and a rationalist view prevailed. The people of an advanced industrialised society, it was thought, were only prepared to believe in things which could be measured and observed. And yet, while the churches were emptying, people were still appealing to mysterious forces. They invented ceremony and observance of a kind which did not necessarily mention the word God but nevertheless followed the language of religion. They read the stars, claimed to experience good and bad energies. They set up floral shrines to accident victims on roadside verges. They talked of fate. When the slump began, these beliefs and superstitions came together to re-establish a tradition of collective worship.

'It needn't have been Christianity which benefited from this desire to worship, and in some places it wasn't. There are several towns, I have learned, where astrology has become the dominant belief system. In those places people get together with great solemnity to receive learned opinions as to the messages of the stars. In one such town – it may be Middlesbrough – astrology gained a following after an explosion in an abandoned chemical works. Rumours rapidly circulated that a medium had predicted the disaster and, impressed by this piece of prescience, the population turned to her for further wisdom. In parts of the West Country, paganism holds sway: though I have never seen them myself, there is talk of midsummer ceremonies involving thousands of people. Yet in most places, religious observance is now based around the parish church: people simply turned back to the religious institution that was closest to them. But there is one thing about christianity which has proved especially suited to our age: its emphasis on repentance. It is widely accepted these days that the age which immediately preceded our own was an evil one, for which mankind must do penance. There are strong elements of paganism in the religion practised now – in that the earth, the mountains, the rivers are held in great reverence – but they are worshipped as the creations of God. When people bow their heads in prayer, they are effectively apologising to God for defiling his creation.

'It was interesting to see how congregations developed. Each week, as the economy sank, huddles of new families would appear at services, dazed. Many of them had barely set foot in a church before. They followed every word, not quite knowing whether to take the words used in the service literally or not. Rapidly, as the new people outnumbered the old, the emphasis of worship began to change. What moved the new recruits was what the church had to say on the question of wealth and greed. I was chaplain in a village not far from here at the time, and it took me a while to work out what people wanted: a denunciation of the consumer society which they felt had let them down. They had spent their lives trying to better themselves financially, but had seen much of that wealth evaporate. They had lost their pensions, their savings and their homes. Now they wanted to hear any teaching which appeared to condemn the accumulation of material goods. They wanted to hear money-lenders denounced. They loved to be told – over and over again – that it is harder for a camel to pass through the eye of a needle than it is for a rich man to enter the kingdom of heaven. This was what they conceived christianity to be about, or at least what they wished it to be about:

the rejection of commerce. To a certain extent it was possible to satisfy them on this, but the literature with which we conducted our services was not generous with relevant material. So it became necessary to generate some.

'The result was the mass of tall stories now known as the third testament. Christianity became creative again. Freelance priests wrote morality tales about bankers who were punished for their love of money and global capitalists who were condemned to burn in hell for their sins committed against fellow man. You will have heard in church many times the parable about the three brothers who one day are presented each with ten thousand pounds. The first one shares it with his neighbours, who buy land and establish a commune, which flourishes. The second invests it for retirement and sees his money eaten away by the greed of the men who manage his pension fund. The third takes it to a bank and uses it to secure a huge loan to start a business which collapses, loading him with impossible debts and ruining him. Many assume this to be an ancient tale, but it is not; it is an invention of the past 20 years. In fact I would go as far as to say that it runs contrary to a very similar tale contained in the bible which I knew as a child.

'Christianity has absorbed many of the quasi religions which had seemed to replace it during the industrial age. In order that new dogma should not stand out from the ancient text, it has been couched in language which, 50 years ago, would have been considered archaic. "Eat not the vegetable which has been fertilized with chemicals not born of the Earth," is one passage often recited in church these days, "but only that which has been nurtured with manure or composted matter. Eat not the chicken that has been confined to a small space, only that which has had space to run. Burn not the fuel that is found within the Earth; for the sake of the planet burn only that which is gathered from the land." I could go on.

'When it became clear the direction in which people's interests were moving, huge numbers of ambitious people, many of whom had lost jobs in commerce, moved into the church. Many of them had been atheists and knew very little about christianity. Yet they were quick learners, who had been schooled in the arts of presentation and argument and had developed great preaching skills. Some entered the closed religious communities which now proliferate in remote areas of country. Others set up in the towns and took to teaching, each attempting to outdo the other in the severity of their doctrines. The liberalisation of the church was quickly reversed. Criminals, adulterers, usurers, those who had aborted children were told that they faced eternal damnation. The rules which have emerged over time are not entirely consistent from one part of the country to another. In some places drug-takers are put to death; in others, the smoking of exotic weeds is so accepted that it has been incorporated into services. I know of churches where communion now involves bread, wine – and a cannabis joint which is deemed to be the breath of Christ.

'The form of religious observance which developed was harsher than that seen in these islands for hundreds of years. Christians who refused to take the resurrection literally were denounced as heretics. Usurers, scientists, unmarried mothers and their children were assaulted. Those who visited gyms were denounced for their obsession with their bodies, atheists were condemned in public, computer experts were harangued for talking the language of the devil. In the industrial age it had been presumed that worshippers could be attracted to the church only through the adoption of liberal attitudes. It was believed that in order to retain their following, religious folk needed to blend their beliefs with the lifestyle choices of the masses. Yet the opposite proved the case: in a time of great confusion, it is dogma and hellfire which has proved the attraction.

'It was inevitable that there should have been clamour for a second coming. And how it has happened! If you believe the tales, Christ has popped up all over England. Priests are regularly called out by excited parents who have noticed a twinkle in the eye of their new-born son and wish for guidance as to whether this might be the arrival of the Christ-child. Most tales are short-lived, but some persist. A couple of years ago there was a rumour that a second son of God had been born in Leicestershire. Many made the journey to search for evidence, but were disappointed. After some months the rumour was quashed; it turned out that local illiterates has mistaken the "child wrapped in swaddling clothes" for "the child raised in Swadlincote", a local village. They had told their neighbours, who had told neighbours until the whole locality had learned of a wondrous child born in Swadlincote. It may seem foolish, but it is quite typical of the errors which are made these days. The fact that people travel so little these days has made their horizons smaller: many have translated the Holy Lands to their own corner of England. People take place names literally. There was a Welsh hamlet by the name of Sodom: the invention of Victorian romantics. A dozen or so years ago, it is widely told, a mob who took the name literally burned the village to the ground.

'Perhaps it ought to be my duty as a priest to scotch this nonsense: to try to keep people to stick to the old teachings. But like many priests, I daren't. There is great danger in not following the demands of your congregation. You can never be certain that your flock is not about to turn on you. The resurgence of faith over the past years has been dangerous and unpredictable: the leaders are not in control. Elderly priests who have suggested to people that they should not take the gospel literally have in some cases been exiled or slain.

'But many will take the risks for the priesthood is one of the few professions which can offer you a full belly. As a priest I have never been in want; I cannot walk far down a street without being accosted by poor wretches who wish me to pray for them, offer ministry to them, even cure them. There may be some who resent the material well-being of the priesthood, but I have much to be grateful for.'

9

Whether you be pleased or distressed to hear of the current condition of mankind, it is as well that you did not awake in Stevenage. It is not that the town is poor, that there are violent gangs on every corner, that the people are hungry and emaciated, that disease is rife, that commerce has collapsed, that ignorance is endemic, that the social improvements of the industrial age have vanished. It is not that the people of Stevenage will ply you with awful tales of decay. These things are true of many other towns, but not of Stevenage. The reason you were better off not awakening in the town is that there are no people there at all. Stevenage is the wasteland you maybe imagined in the days when doom-mongers spun us tales of biological warfare: buildings, roads intact, but the human population mysteriously spirited away. You can wander up and down the concrete boulevards of this long-lost industrial empire all day and you will be lucky to find so much as a passing traveller. There are said to be families still braving it out in the outer regions of the town, but we did not see them as we sought out the railway station. We saw just startled cats.

The question of population is one which has exercised scholars greatly in recent years. There are some who believe nine-tenths of the human population has been lost since the end of the industrial age. That is almost certainly an exaggeration. I believe it to be more like half; more in the great cities of the industrial age; much less, probably, in the remoter regions of Europe and Asia. It is impossible to know. But the loss of population has been very unequal. There are some places, such as the prairies of Norfolk, where the soil is good, that the numbers of people have very likely increased. You can pass through villages where nothing seems amiss: crowds of urchins will surround you and stare at you and follow you as you make your progress. There are towns where small cottages brim with ten or 15 residents, exploiting each other for their warmth. But there are other places from which, for obscure reasons, the population has entirely decamped. If there is a general rule, it is 'last in, first out'. The ancient places, where the streets are narrow, the buildings stand close together and are not far removed from open fields, are well-populated. People feel safer there, food is closer at hand and they are invariably situated in places close to fresh water. The newer neighbourhoods, which were designed around the railway and the motor-car, have shed their populations. It is possible to find a few families living in the underpasses and picking about for food on the roundabouts, but for the most part people today view the wide open spaces of the late industrial age town as inhospitable places to live. The words 'new town' have become synonymous with 'burial ground': to say that a friend 'has gone to the new town' means he has died. The old overspill settlements are rivalled in their emptiness only by the former coastal resorts, whose aged populations rapidly died off at the end of the industrial age, leaving behind nobody to sustain them other than a few roughened fishermen.

It is easy to be shocked by the appearance of a place like Stevenage and imagine some apocalyptic terror. But the role of premature death in the reduction of the population over the past few decades can easily be overstated. As important was the collapse in the birth rate. In places such as Stevenage there came a point at which the remaining residents were so elderly and so few that they gave up attempting to support themselves and fled to neighbouring settlements where at least they could expend their few remaining energies working for others.

As we approached the railway station at Stevenage it became obvious that we were in for disappointment: the train service to London which had been promised in the letter inviting me to the exhibition was a fiction. There were trains in the station, but they were empty vessels, abandoned years before and buried up to their roofs in thistles and young trees. It is possible that 30 years had elapsed since they were last used. There was a period of a few years when in spite of the collapse of many businesses and services, small bands of volunteers maintained the railways. They saw it their duty to attempt to preserve what they could of industrial machinery – at great danger from attack. But eventually the machinery grew decrepit and defeated them. Some time later, a band of Progressive thugs must have romped through Stevenage and set the station alight, for many of the carriages had been burnt-out.

The non-existence of the train service did not displease us all. Bump made it quite clear that had the trains been operational he would have refused to travel in any case. 'These were vehicles of oppression,' he said. 'The railway accidents: there is no more disgusting episode in history. The millions who were arbitrarily selected to be sacrificed! That people would be squashed into these trains and then the things crashed to mangle and maim them!'

I have become used to such outbursts from the young, whose minds have been poisoned against the industrial age, but I could not let this stand. 'Do you not understand the nature of an accident?' I asked Bump. 'It is just like these days when a man is swept away by flooding, or killed by a falling tree. It was not possible to cope with all the dangers of industrial machinery.'

Bump became quite angry. 'Floods and falling trees are natural ways to die,' he protested. 'The railway accidents were not natural: they were man-made ways of killing. If they were not intentional, then why did they keep on happening? These were crimes committed by engineers.'

I shook my head. The word 'engineer' is used these days to denote a person of murderous intent. It has become common practice – we saw such a shrine on the road to Knebworth – to hold services to commemorate the victims of the engineers on the sites of ancient rail and road accidents; sites which ever since the industrial age have been maintained by the leaving of flowers. Locals will gather, say prayers to the dead, light candles and burn effigies of cars, trains and planes. They are taken quite seriously, these occasions; it has become a grave offence to deny that these disasters happened, to suggest anything other than that they were deliberately staged by engineers. Few famous individuals of the industrial age have retained their celebrity in the current age, but the victims of accidents are better known than most: their names are still recited at these services, and in one of two cases they have been canonised. Saint Lucy, who was named on the shrine at Knebworth, was, we discovered, a girl mown down by a runaway truck many years ago. Her teddy bear has become an object of great reverence.

There is a tremendous folklore built around the industrial way of death. Some distance on, while crossing the old railway viaduct at Welwyn, we came across a group of children at play. They were of an age – eight or nine – at which it was possible to converse with them without incurring a sense of hostility: adults would have chased us from their patch. We learned much from them. They were taking it in turns to dangle each other over the brick parapet, being held upside down by their feet, staring at what is perhaps a 100 foot drop. At this they showed no fear, or at least they took pride in pretending not to. It became clear that there was built into their games a view of the industrial age as a time of great terror. 'I'll be the lorry,' one of them said. 'No, I want to be the lorry, you be the train,' countered another, before they embarked on a game which involved running into each other at great speed. Their mothers, they told us, disapproved strongly of this game: they said that the railway accidents were not something of which to make fun. Then these boys went onto another game, where they had to pin each other down and stuff fistfuls of dirt into each other's mouths, before saying:. 'Ugh, you've eaten the beefburger – you're dead'. 'Ring 'o ring 'o roses,' one of them began to chant, 'Poison up your noses . . . a tissue, a tissue . . . we all fall down.' I asked the oldest of the children what he thought the rhyme meant. Easy, he told me: 'It's about the days when there was so much pollution that nobody could breathe, and they all used to die.'

Studying all this with great care was Dr Anders Hoeffel, whose legal mind was greatly challenged. 'It is difficult for me to decide how I should feel,' he said, once we had left the children and were on our way. 'Despair, bewilderment – or shame? I cannot forget that as a young lawyer I played my part in promoting a certain awareness of the hazards of the industrial era. A large part of my business was in winning compensation for those maimed in accidents and disfigured by environmental diseases. My clients were the victims of the industrial age: those whom chance had sacrificed so that the rest of us could enjoy the luxuries of the time. Except that my profession recognised no such thing as chance: our business depended upon the identification of blame, and so we tended to view all accidents as deliberate. There was money to be made out of fear, to be sure. I did my utmost to prick the confidence of those who had an unswerving faith in industrial advance. But this was not what I had in mind, not this shuddering rejection of industrialisation. My business was a humanitarian one, about keeping humans the masters of the industrialised world, not retreating to the peasanthood we witness now. How sad to think that human rights would have led to this.'

'Please, tell me,' said Abdul, 'if you do not mind me interrupting. But this is important to me. It is one of my ambitions to discover the original human rights charter. It is said that these tablets of stone are buried in Geneva, or in Strasbourg, or in Brussels – that is the other place mentioned. Tell me, have you seen these tablets? Do they really exist?'

Dr Hoeffel chuckled. 'That is too literal, I am afraid. There were no stone tablets, but, yes, I can see why you should think of them being committed to stone, for they had similarities with the commandments – though they were commandments turned on their heads, so that they read "thou shalt not have done to thou. . .".'

'What moral laziness!' cried Bump. 'It is for this reason that the industrial age was doomed.'

'We did not think ourselves as lazy,' said Dr Hoeffel. 'We were working firmly in the Christian tradition. But Christian morality on its own had failed: what had it done for the poor, the dispossessed and the minorities, as they were called? Where in the commandments did it say: "thou shalt not discriminate against those more unfortunate than yourself?" Christian morality was very strong on saving your own soul, but it did not speak for those who might become trampled-upon in the process. Thus we came up with human rights, a code derived, so it seemed, from some ethereal yet godless presence, but which were rational, and free of superstition.'

'The evil of it is immense,' said Bump. 'You speak of an ethereal presence, yet these rules of yours, the code by which human beings would eternally be judged, was in reality hammered out by gluttonous international worthies who flew about in aircraft and consumed great meals paid for by the hard work of the poor.'

'You have a point,' said Dr Hoeffel. 'How astonishingly naïve it all seems now, that we were creating an eternal moral code, when in fact our minds were trapped in the politics of the time. What does the "right to work?" mean now, when there are slave-masters falling over themselves to purchase your labour? As human rights' lawyers, we were overwhelmed by our early successes. The lot of women in the western world improved. The innocent were less often wrongly convicted of offences. Yet what answers did we have to evil? The great circus that was the law became very good at helping win compensation for those who fell on uneven paving stones, yet in saving children from being blown apart in the madness of some distant civil war, and preventing dissidents from being systematically eradicated by some distant dictatorship, it proved feeble. Religion is much better than the law at righting these kinds of injustice, for punishment can be deferred to a subsequent life. Look at the Church now: its strictures scream out from the walls of peasants' cottages once more. That we might have achieved the same with the Right to Work and the Right to a Fair Hearing! But we were operating in such different conditions that it is inevitable we failed. We had to deal with that ungovernable thing, public opinion.

'What do they mean now, the words 'public opinion?'. When you say somebody is suffering from "an attack of public opinion" it means they have gone mad. How perverse it seems these days, the idea that every adult should be expected to form a view on current events: ordinary people do not now burden their minds with matters beyond their family and neighbours. Yet back in the industrial age, people could not seem to help themselves forming crude ideas on the wider world. For a time I believed it to be part of a process of enlightenment: that an informed public was as near a perfect form of political leadership as had ever existed. I was not to foresee how rapidly and how venomously would this public opinion come to be mobilised against my profession. Look at how we lawyers are remembered now: as a bizarre sect charged with the grave heresy of rewriting the commandments.'

'I do not understand,' said Abdul. 'You say that the public turned against the lawyers. This is quite different from my reading of the industrial era, in which the lawyer is held up as a hero. You must help me establish the myth from the truth. Tell me, was

there or was there not a lawyer by the name of Robin Hood who
sued the rich to give compensation to the poor?'

'Myth, all myth,' said Dr Hoeffel. 'Robin Hood is a much older
tale; he does not date from the age of human rights. Though
perhaps it is true we lawyers thought of ourselves as playing a
similar role.'

'That is a disgraceful untruth,' said Bump. 'Lawyers never had
anything to do with Robin Hood. Robin Hood was an
environmental activist who seized food and drugs grown by
multinational corporations and distributed them amongst the
poor.'

'We can argue over Robin Hood all day,' said Dr Hoeffel.
'Everybody can claim him and everybody will. There are
hundreds of Robin Hoods on this island. It is true that for some
time lawyers were cast in his role: the championing of the little
guy. For a while, films were made of our exploits. The poor, the
dispossessed; they put their faith in us where all else had failed
them. It did not save us, though, from the distrust and contempt
which was later to be heaped upon us. As a young man, I believed
that we were instilling in educated people a more rational
approach to the subject of crime and punishment. I was a fool.
The rule of the mob was never quite to leave us; on the contrary,
it was accentuated by the existence of newspapers and television
pictures. Initially, the industrial age brought with it a sense of lost
community; it was implied that human relations were being
damaged by the ease of travel. The pre-industrial village, where
every man knew each other and knew what each other were up
to, was replaced by an anonymous society in which most people
one encountered were strangers. The simpler society with a more
direct moral code was much-mourned, and there came a time
when people felt the urge to regain it. This they did in a most
brutal way. I once had the job of defending a suspected child-
abuser. It was a very promising job. There was nothing but
rumour to substantiate the crime, let alone the involvement of the

accused. The evidence had so clearly been put into the child's head that it was laughable. In very little time the accused was acquitted and went free. Justice, it seemed, had been served. But that was not the end of it; far from it. In the eyes of the public, which had been fed gossip about the case on a daily basis, two grave crimes had been committed: one by the accused and a second by the court in acquitting him. At the time, the public had a particular distaste for this type of crime and treated the mere rumour of guilt as evidence enough. Within a fortnight, the freed man was hunted down and killed, pushed from a motorway bridge in the middle of the night.

'These incidents were repeated on many occasions. In time, those who hunted an acquitted man became quite brazen about it. After executing their deed, they would announce to the world that "natural justice" had been done. There steadily emerged two parallel systems of law: the official law, as overseen by the courts, and natural justice as practised by thugs, egged on by crowds. The police became quite powerless to stop this practice, and, to save themselves from danger, began quite willingly to release accused men to natural justice – in other words, to turn them out of police stations into the hands of mobs. If cases did go to the courts they were treated as no more than pre-trial hearings: an acquittal would invariably lead to the evidence being assessed by the public at large and, should it call for further action, a willing executioner would quickly emerge.

'In the end, lawyers, too, became targets: to defend a client successfully began to bring with it the threat of a beating. There were those lawyers who took a fatalistic attitude and took the punishment which was meted out to them. They would stand by the principles upon which they learned their craft, and free the suspect against whom there was insufficient evidence. They were mostly murdered. A greater number removed themselves from legal service, taking up lowly-paid jobs and concealing their history. Others – and I am sorry to say that I belonged to this category for a while – allowed themselves to be carried along by the practitioners of natural justice. Though I had never practised as such before, I assumed the role of a judge; a freelance judge who went about dispensing whatever justice the public wished to hear. It was a dreadful episode of my life, but there was the question of self-preservation. I console myself that I was merely rubber-stamping the prejudices of the masses, whose minds were made up but who nevertheless sought the legitimacy of a trained lawyer. If I sent petty thieves to their deaths – and I do not wish even to entertain the possibility that some of them may have been innocent – I comfort myself with the certain knowledge that the same would have happened to them whether I had been there or not.

'I travelled about, and for some months was treated quite royally. I would be summoned in great secrecy and told that a trial was to be held at such and such a place. A car, or in later days a cart, would be sent, and I would be taken to a barn or a disused warehouse where a crowd had gathered. The police, such as they remained, were unable to keep up. The accused would be pronounced guilty and beaten or executed within half an hour. Within an hour the crowd had dispersed, with sealed lips, to taverns and their homes. I did not dare to stay to enjoy the hospitality I was offered, nor did I usually remain long enough to witness the public executions which I had helped to bring about. All I can say is that I would never have imagined how comfortably mankind would have slipped back into this once-obsolete practice.

'Whatever happened to the education, the enlightenment of the industrial age? Ah, for many people, this was enlightenment: the arcane beliefs and rituals of liberal society swept aside by reason. It is seen as nonsensical, these days, that criminals could ever have been released after having been given a "life" sentence, that the criminal record of a defendant could have been withheld from the jury during a trial. Natural justice was viewed as a reformation, the culmination of several hundred years' march towards democracy.

'When people of the industrial age imagined the future, they sometimes foresaw chaos: the total breakdown of law, a descent into "every man for himself". Yet that is quite different from what has happened: the rule of law did not break down, it has been replaced by what in some ways is a more orderly system. Judgements are instant: they do not drag out for years as once they did. There is far greater certainty as to the fate of suspect brought forward, no appeals, no awkward clauses; though agonisingly the law does tend to change from town to town. On the matter of drugs in particular, this puts a traveller at great risk. How is one supposed to know, upon entering a tavern where drinkers are stoned on opium tea, that the act of swigging fermented blackberry juice from a hipflask would be sufficient to have you put on trial, while in the next town the law might be the other way about: alcohol accepted, opium a capital offence?

'My spell as a dispenser of mob law could not last. There came the day when I was called upon to pass sentence upon a man accused of smoking a pipe full of dried nettles. No sooner had I passed sentence on the poor wretch – he was to receive a beating – than it became clear that he had support among the crowd. I had misread the people: the majority of them had wanted him acquitted in order to humiliate his accusers, who might then be subject to a counter-charge of sniffing from pots of glue. There was uproar when I passed my sentenced. People surged forwards to force the executioner and his dogs from the room – the setting of dogs upon a prisoner being a favoured means of execution in these parts. The crowd merely chanted "appeal, appeal", and would gladly have torn me limb from limb. But I took my chance and slipped from the crowd, and vowed to keep away from trials for as long as I lived.'

Dr Hoeffel might have kept his promise had we not been distracted by a loud cheer as we passed through the remains of Welwyn Garden City. It came from an old football stadium, leading us to wonder whether some kind of sport was being played within. There was, of a sort. We entered to discover 500 or so people attending a trial, presided over by a 'mediator' appointed by the Lord of the Manor of Welwyn. The mediator, dressed in a long cloak, sat on a chair in the long grass close to where the goalmouth would once have been. 'Order!' he cried as the cheering subsided. The crowd fell quiet and a hunch-shouldered figure was led before him.

The mediator asked him politely to stand up straight, but he said regretfully that he could not. 'I've been like this for a dozen years,' he said. 'And it's getting worse. My back is becoming more arched by the day, and there is nothing I can do to stop it. It takes me two hours to get out of bed in the morning. I am of such little use these days that my wife must do all the work around the house, and go out to fetch food from the woods. I am in constant pain. I have visited a healer but he says there is only one thing which could alleviate my condition.'

'And that is?' asked the mediator.

'I must pray for the evil to be undone, and for those who inflicted it upon me to be punished. I know the cause of my misfortune. I used to live near a large chimney, and I have been crippled by dioxins spewed out of it. Poisonous clouds of these dioxins used to descend on my house. I could see them, smell them, feel them tickle the back of my throat. It was those dioxins alright. There is no other explanation.'

'Have the owners of this chimney been located?'

'They have long since gone, I'm afraid. There is no trace of them.'

Without seeking further witnesses, the mediator moved swiftly to a verdict. 'He wouldn't dare do otherwise,' whispered Dr Hoeffel in my ear, 'for he would run the risk of being murdered by the crowd.'

'The cause of your problems is proven beyond doubt,' said the mediator. 'The responsibility of dioxins for conditions such as yours is well known. In the absence of the owners of this chimney, I can do nothing other than to sentence them to eternal suffering for inflicting their pollution upon the people.'

As a further cheer erupted, I noticed that a woman sat next to me was sticking pins into a small rag doll. What was she doing, I asked? 'It's how we punish the ones who don't turn up to face the charges,' she said. 'It would be much better for them if they did turn up. They would get a kicking, but they would in most likelihood survive. There is no surviving this, though: this is eternal.' I looked around and noticed that others, too, had dolls upon which they were inflicting the most savage punishments.

Several similar cases followed. One elderly, twitching woman demanded that her former employers be condemned for causing her to suffer repetitive strain injury. The mediator duly obliged and there was another round of doll-stabbing. A crumpled man in his seventies demanded that the makers of beefburgers be killed for causing him to suffer heart disease. There were accident victims, sufferers from stress, people who complained of overwork. Then came a woman with her two children, both of whom were suffering from chilblains. 'It's the extreme climate!' she screamed. 'It's the global warming that's made my two babies suffer in this way. The weather keeps on going from one extreme to another. It is all because of the oil-burning and coal-burning which went on during the industrial age. The people who are responsible for this must suffer.' Once again the mediator obliged by conferring punishment upon the absent culprits. He then called for silence and another figure was brought before him, this one a stout man in his early 30s. He was accompanied by two guards. 'What is your name?' asked the mediator. 'I'm Tool,' he said.

'And why is Tool here?' the mediator asked the guards.

'He killed his teenage daughter on learning that she was carrying a child,' said the guard.

'And why did you do this, Tool?'

'I didn't mean to do it,' said Tool. 'The truth was I didn't want her in the house. I can't afford an extra mouth to feed. And it was shameful, because it was my brother who fathered the little beast. I pushed the girl out of the door, but she fell on the broken glass in the window and cut herself badly. There was nothing I could do. She collapsed and was gone in five minutes.'

Again, the mediator did not bother to call other witnesses. Instead, he said he would move quickly to a verdict. This was delivered by acclamation, the crowd being invited to shout 'oh-nine-oh-six' or 'oh-nine-oh-seven': the first being code for 'punish him', and the second being code for 'let him go'. Everyone in the crowd was aware of what these cries meant, though it transpired few were aware of their origins. I can only suggest that they derive from parts of numbers rung by respondents to telephone polls in the late industrial age.

There was such a deafening shout of 'oh-nine-oh-six' that I assumed the killer must be on the point of receiving a death sentence. Then, to my surprise, there was an even louder shout of 'oh-nine-oh-seven', and he was freed. It was quite clear to me that some had shouted twice. Why, I asked one of them: a middle aged man who was sitting in front of me. 'I can't possibly say whether he murdered the girl or not because I wasn't there,' he said. 'It is for us to shout, and for God to decide.'

'Are trials held often in this stadium?' I asked him. 'They are once a fortnight,' he said. 'Today's is typical. There is very little crime these days. There cannot be more than one murder a month in this town, and no more than a dozen thefts. It is quite unlike the old days, when there was mass slaughter every day. My father used to show me an old newspaper and tell me: "look, I've totted them up and there are 273 deaths spoken about in this paper – all in one day!" No, crime is mercifully rare these days. But there is still this terrible backlog of cases from forty or fifty years ago. When they will ever be cleared I quite despair. It was so dreadful a time for injustice, the industrial age.'

The final case of the day was that of a thin, wild-eyed teenager who had been accused of stealing birds which had been trapped by his neighbour. The accused had little to say: he could hardly speak. But his accuser produced some compelling evidence, to which the unfortunate boy was seen to be nodding. The lad appearing to confirm his guilt, there was no need to go any further, the mediator said. 'I duly pass sentence, and ask for the pitch to be cleared.'

The mediator, along with several officials, guards and spectators then withdrew to seats up in the stands, leaving the convicted thief standing alone in the long grass, terrified. A whistle was blown, and from each corner of the stadium emerged four or five young thugs, wearing nothing but shorts and large pairs of boots. The accused turned and began to run, but quickly realised that he was encircled. Before he had gone far, one of the thugs kicked his feet from under him and he fell forwards into the grass, to the sound of much cheering and laughter. At some length, he pulled himself upright and began to run again, though was quickly hacked down, and this time remained there, whimpering. His ordeal was only relieved when a mediator came onto the pitch waving a red flag: a sign that the punishment was to end and the accused was to be removed.

We could face no more. As the crowd rose from their seats to cheer once more, we sneaked out of a back entrance and made our way from Welwyn Garden City as quickly as we could. We kept going until we found an abandoned house, where we slept on damp mattresses, being woken up from time to time by the screams of each others' nightmares.

10

The closer we came to London, the more ragged the people became. The flushed faces of Royston's meat markets were replaced by thin, drawn figures who sat by the roadside or who walked the streets pushing supermarket trolleys full of possessions. We were accosted by elderly hawkers trying to sell us all manner of goods which they had pillaged from old shops. Others begged or laboured in roadside allotments, breaking the soil with rusty spades and any other implements which they could lay their hands upon. There was a defeated appearance to this mainly elderly populace. We saw few children and still fewer smiles. It was to these parts, the broken ring of country once known as the green belt, to which millions of Londoners fled at the end of the industrial age, and the signs of this exodus are still evident. In places, the motorways are blocked by eternal traffic jams of rusty and broken vehicles which have stood there ever since their drivers embarked on a final, fruitless journey to who knows where. In the final months of the industrial age a terrorist act, an outbreak of disease or a food shortage would provoke a wave of refugees from the cities to the surrounding country. Such evacuations turned out to be cataclysms in themselves, for they invariably ended up with pile-ups and knuckle fights. Unable to progress further, many people settled here, in Hertfordshire's refugee camps.

The camps have not disappeared as such. They have evolved. Organisation has been brought to them. The ambitious have left, the troublesome have been driven away. The remaining compliant, hungry mass of humanity has settled down to a life of drudgery and, effectively in most cases, imprisonment. There is order in these feudal encampments perhaps as there is order nowhere else in the British Isles. The lords who run them have, quite by accident, managed to develop a medieval system of governance. Their servants are made to divide their time between agricultural labour and military service; the latter of which consists of guarding their camps from incursions by hungry outsiders.

We had intended to steer a passage between feudal encampments, but there was little hope. After Hatfield, we took a left turn into the woods. At first, all was quiet. We clambered through the undergrowth, chancing upon an old woodland track which seemed to lie well away from any habitation. There were squirrels, rabbits and garden birds by the hundred. We spotted the droppings of badgers, wild boar, and, we suspected, the odd panther or puma. The evidence of big cats did not worry us unduly – these animals have become quite common in the countryside, their ancestors having escaped from zoos at the end of the industrial age. But we were then unnerved by the sight of several mongrel dogs and the sound of high-pitched whistles in the distance.

We had gone perhaps half an hour into the thicket when, with little warning, we were disturbed by several men carrying large clubs. They were dressed in a distinctive uniform: small luminous orange jackets like those worn by the railwaymen of the industrial age. 'This is private property!' shouted one of the men. There was no chance to escape. From the undergrowth emerged several more thugs in the same orange jackets. 'What are you doing here?' asked the leader. 'It is forbidden to enter these woods. They are owned by the Duke.'

'The Duke?' I asked. 'Which duke?'

'He is known only as the Duke. There are no other dukes. The Duke would not allow it. I demand you tell me what you are doing here.'

'We are trying to find the way to Potters Bar. Is this not the way? Or perhaps you could direct us to the public road.'

'There is no public road to Potters Bar. To go there you must ask the permission of the Duke. He owns all the land between here and there and will not be messed with.'

'But there must be a way through. There was always a public road to Potters Bar.'

'There is none. And I know these woods.'

With little chance to protest, we were rounded up by the thugs and led through the trees into a clearing. Before us was a large Tudor mansion, guarded by yet more thugs in orange jackets who were marching backwards and forwards, their clubs held in their left hands and resting against their shoulders. In front of the house, several bearded figures dressed in the remains of tattered old business suits were weeding a large lawn. We were then taken through a kitchen garden where stooped figures were tending carrots, radishes and herbs. From there we were led through a gateway and across a field into what had clearly once been an upmarket housing estate. It consisted of a dozen or so houses, scattered about a cul-de-sac. Fifty years ago they would have been set in neat gardens with two or three cars on the driveways. But the gardens had been allowed to run to seed and there were no cars. Stooped men and women sat in doorways or on rotting benches, chewing blades of grass or any other object which came to hand.

'This is where our executives sleep,' our captor informed us. By 'executive', we soon learned, he did not mean the senior manager who went by that term when the houses were built. He meant a labourer of low status. We were led into one of the houses and found its rooms had been given over exclusively to dormitories, their floors covered with foul-smelling mattresses. Even the former bathrooms had been converted to dormitories; the residents using instead the surrounding woods as toilets. Washing, we learned, was performed in the nearby streams – and only in summer. On the mattresses, a few sick or otherwise listless individuals were lying, doubled-up, holding parts of their bodies in pain. Our captor stopped to speak to several of the figures, asking them which of their colleagues had most recently died and where they had slept. One by one, these vacated mattresses were allotted to us. Mine smelled so foul that I spent only a few minutes on it before taking to the hard floor instead.

After half an hour we were offered food. We were led to a large barn, fitted with dozens of tables formed into long benches, and offered thin gruel. Around the benches were squashed several hundred men, women and children. Here, we were to meet some of our fellow inmates, many of whom seemed unexpectedly contended with their lot. 'I've been here seven years or so now,' said one of them, Jack. 'I can't complain. I've done well. When I came here I was just an executive. Now I've been appointed a serf – which means I've got my own allotment and I work three days for myself, three days for the common good. On those three days, I can grow what I want and the duke only takes one tenth of it. There are opportunities here, to be sure, if you are prepared to take them. But there are those who just don't get on.'

'Who doesn't reminisce about the old days when men worked with photocopiers and computers?' said another inmate, Sam. 'But there is a lot we have now that we didn't have then. Who got to eat fresh vegetables every day back in the industrial times, eh? We only had poor, rubbery food from cardboard packets in those days, so unpalatable it made people throw up. Sure, the work is a bit monotonous. I can't say I really like digging the land. Working in an office was more fulfilling in many ways. But who would really choose the dangers and insecurities of life 50 years ago over the camaraderie here? Several times a day we all gather by the water pump, have a drink and a gossip. You must join us. It has become almost like gathering at the office photocopier.'

These were educated people, we quickly realised. Even the younger of them had some knowledge of the industrial age, and talked about it regularly. All had a thoughtful outlook upon their condition. After supper, they sat and talked, smoking what I took to be a tobacco made from dried leaves. Some played games, at which they had acquired great skill and had in some cases adapted to their circumstances. In one corner several sat playing a version of bridge adapted to take account of the fact that the jack of diamonds and several other cards were missing from the pack. Others played a version of chess, but with missing pieces made up by any objects upon which they could lay their hands. They had incorporated their former occupations into the game in an ironic form: the 'pawns' had been renamed 'accountants' or 'clerks', while the king had been renamed 'the duke'. Other games had been derived from the computer games of former times, and involved the obliteration of aliens. It was strange to hear people talking of extra-terrestrial life: aliens no longer feature in popular culture as they once did. In fact, I hadn't heard the concept of aliens mentioned for many years. It is as if the flying saucers ceased to buzz Planet Earth the moment that mankind himself ceased to fly.

In one corner, watched-over by several guards, sat a lanky individual writing his diary. Every so often, usually when the diarist broke into a smile, a guard would stoop down and look at the page. 'What does that say?' he would demand, whereupon the diarist would mutter something about an incident involving a dropped egg or somebody's shirt which had been ripped on a thorn. Writing is widely considered a subversive act these days, and I suspected that the diarist was fobbing-off his illiterate guards. What plans was he hatching, I wondered, what rude remarks was he making about his captors? But, no, when I got close I could see that he really was writing about dropped eggs and ripped shirts.

'We are not wealthy here, but look what we've gained over the years,' said the diarist, whose name we discovered was Rupert. 'You will never have anything stolen here, and there is no violence, providing you keep within the rules. You can let your children roam about freely knowing they will come to no harm: you couldn't have done that back in the old days, could you? The day is organised for you here. There is none of the worry about finding a job and holding it down: there is work here for anyone who is prepared to do it. I had ulcers before I came here. I used to sell pharmaceutical drugs for a living, and I wouldn't recommend that to anyone. I know it sounds glamorous to young ears, but it wasn't.'

After some time speaking among the residents, we were surprised to be invited to the private chambers of the Duke. He turned out to be a tall man of partial West Indian extraction, who sat in a cloak at the far end of the room. The experience was not unlike walking into Julius Holder's private chambers, though the Duke was clearly a man of more extravagant tastes. His walls were hung with paintings of some antiquity, while several tables carried an eclectic mix of artefacts, from 18th century candlesticks to late industrial age novelties like lava lamps and executive toys. I was expecting him to have a severe temper, though he turned out to be quite genial. He began with a number of formal enquiries as to the purpose of our travelling; which, daring not to mention our journey to the exhibition, we said was in aid of finding work. Then he began to talk about his collection of art. In this, he had considerable knowledge, recalling the names of obscure 18th century artists and enlightening us on the finer points of their technique.

'The collection has been with the family for several generations,' he told us. 'And I have continued to add to it as I see fit. It is a great privilege to own these great works. I think it is only right that I share the enjoyment of them with others."

'How did your family come by the collection?' I enquired.

'It was built up from the proceeds of their endeavours,' said the

Duke. 'My ancestors worked hard for their status. They were muggers on the North London Line. They had control from Stratford to Hampstead. Look, it is recorded on the family crest.' And he showed us a coat of arms which had at its centre a hooded head. 'I still have my great grandfather's mugging clothes and I wear them on ceremonial occasions. Life was much rougher and more basic in those days, of course. It was every man for himself. And my ancestors, thankfully, were able to hold their own. But out of it has grown civilisation.' Then he offered us some parsnip wine, served in fine crystal glasses.

Soon, the Duke got down to business. 'What brings you onto my estate?' he asked. 'I take it that you are looking for work?'

'We have been told that there is work to be had near St Albans,' I said. 'But I am sure we took a wrong turn. We lost the road and found ourselves in woods, which it appears belong to you.'

'The woods are mine for some distance about. It is a large estate. I have upwards of eight hundred people working for me here. It is good work, though it is not without its risks. To the south of my estate you come rapidly upon the frontier. It is necessary to defend ourselves from raiders who see my cultivated land as a convenience store. They are uncouth people who grow nothing themselves but treat my birds as if they were their own. Of course, this can not be tolerated, and we have these people put down. I gather from the way in which you gave yourselves up to my men, and the fact that you came from the north rather than the south, that you are not yourselves poachers. That is good, and I shall see that you are treated well. There is no need for you to travel to St Albans. There is work for you here. You will be registered as executives and shown to your quarters.'

'For how long will we be expected to stay?'

'Your contract will be for two years. You will be wanted for military service one day a week. After two years, when your contract comes up for renewal, you will be given the opportunity to take a smallholding of your own. There is no need for you to want to leave. Your safety here will be assured. This is a large estate, and with the help of our foot soldiers can be kept secure.'

My fellow travellers and I looked at each other, and I forget who it was who tentatively then asked: 'Is it possible for anybody to leave?'

'It is not always easy for us to keep tracks of everybody,' said the Duke. 'We lose people from time to time; they wander off and sometimes they do not come back. It is not a sensible option, however, for people to choose to leave. If people do not report for meals, their quarters are searched. If we cannot find them there, we let the dogs into the woods. Most of those who escape are caught quickly. A few stay out for days, but they tend to return when they are hungry. When they have been gone for more than a year we no longer pursue them and they can consider themselves free. Until that time they are under contract here.'

'How many people get out?' asked Alferris.

'Very few,' said the Duke. 'I cannot think of any this year. I think there were two last year, though I remember we also discovered the remains of one youth not three miles away. He died of cold; he was so ill-prepared for his adventure. No, very few choose to leave. Why should they? Everything they need is here. They have food, security and friends. There is structure here. The days are planned. It was my father who impressed upon me the importance of planning and routine. He knew from personal experience: several times when he was a young man he was granted the opportunity to serve in a prison community, and he never forgot the debt he owed to those who sent him there. It was so sad, he told me towards the end of his life, that the prison communities had become so undervalued in the late industrial age. Many lawyers made a low form of living by fighting to keep deserving people out of prison communities. Rather than accept young men into them, the authorities took a perverse pleasure in turning them onto the streets and watching them sink. Was it really necessary to do that? It was such a callous age.'

For three days we laboured according to the instruction of our foreman. There was much to do. There were potatoes to plant, weeds to be pulled by the fistful from the sweating earth. We were given spades, axes and long steel shafts salvaged from the remains of old vehicles, and we were set to work breaking up the soil in a field which had not been cultivated for years. Due to my age, I was excused from much of the work, but instead I was made to keep an eye on the others and to report to the foremen anybody I had seen resting, or even talking to their colleagues. Towards nightfall, I was taken to the kitchens and given work there. As a reward, I expected a feast; yet we were given the same thin gruel as we had been given the evening before. Nobody, however, went hungry. There were large quantities of gruel on offer, and it was eagerly swallowed even by those whom it was making badly flatulent. The inmates seemed to have little inhibition about belching loudly, and the Duke did it frequently throughout the meal.

On the third day we were transferred to construction work. The roof of one of the executive homes had started to leak. Rather than replace the slipped tiles and the warped zinc flashings, the Duke had insisted that the house instead be thatched. Thatch was a superior material to tiles, he believed. I was put under the command of an elderly man who was introduced to me as the 'Master Thatcher', though it soon became clear to me that he knew little about his work. He took the stalks of mildew straw with which he had been supplied, neatly trimmed them and formed them into tidy bundles. But when it came to securing the bundles to the rafters, his amateurishness was revealed. He tried to tie the straw to the roof with lengths of string which soon sprung loose, allowing the bunches of straw to slide down the roof. Then he tried nailing the straw into place, but had little success with this, either.

In scores of years' time, the skill of thatching will no doubt again be mastered, but it was not going to be today. Eventually, the Master Thatcher and I managed to provide the roof with some kind of covering of straw, but that night there was a fierce rainstorm and it leaked badly. 'I take it that you have not been in this trade all your life,' I said to the thatcher when we were sent back to the building the following morning and were accosted by the poor, drenched workers who had spent the night there. 'No,' he told me. 'And I am not sure whether I enjoy the work. But you have to accept the need sometimes to retrain in order to keep up with the times. The younger people here look up to me, though I cannot understand why. This job is something of a comedown for me. I have nothing like the power which I had in my old career. My professionalism was widely respected.'

'What did you do?' I asked.

'I used to work for one of the local councils. I was a building standards officer. They all used to fear me, they did, all the builders in this neighbourhood. They wouldn't try to fool me with shoddy work: they knew it would go straight to the courts. I dealt with the occasional thatched building during my time, which is why I volunteered for this post; my choice lay between thatching and labouring in the fields. I remember some of the methods of thatching from my manuals, but it seems so different now than it did then because you cannot get the right materials any more. A new set of standards will have to be written. It is such a shame that I do not still have my old books. They would have made this work so much easier.'

Though we had been placed in different dormitories and put on different jobs, I managed to meet with other members of my party on several occasions in our first three days at the Duke's encampment. We had but one subject of conversation: escape. It seemed at first sight a simple business: a quick dash through the woods and we would be free. But it became clear from close observation that the woods were thick with guards and dogs. In addition, we discovered that the estate was closed on most sides with coils of rusty barbed wire. Though this would have seemed an insubstantial barrier back in the industrial age, one does not these days take lightly the risk of cutting the skin. As often as not, a deep laceration amounts to a death sentence. We no longer have antibiotics capable of arresting blood poisoning. We may even be worse off than had we never had these medicines in the first place: our constitutions, I suspect, have been weakened by the proliferation of these medicines in the industrial age. It is unwise now to take chances with sharp objects. People go about their outdoor work in thick boots, covered head to toe with thick clothing. Old rubbish dumps, which lie thick with sharp objects, are places which few dare go near.

We had made little progress towards a viable escape plan when, on the third night following our incarceration, we were awoken by a commotion. Amid much shouting and banging, our fellow executives hurriedly rose from their beds and dressed. Over their shirts and shell suits they buttoned bright orange vests. 'What's going on?' I asked a youth who was sleeping on the mattress next to mine. 'Do I have to get up too?' 'Of course,' he said. 'There has been an incursion down on the frontier. We must all get down there at once and stop the people from coming over.'

'Which people?' I asked.

'The people from London. They try to do this every few days. We must all go down and help drive them back.'

I quickly did as I was told. I dressed, and joined the mass of executives on a hectic run along a muddy track through the woods. It would have been better had we marched with some semblance of rhythm, but the executives insisted on jogging, and so we stumbled through the puddles, frequently colliding with each other. Some could not keep up the pace and rested by the side of the track, breathing heavily. They were struck by our guards and forced to continue. Dawn had yet to break and we could barely see where we were going, but after half a mile or so I could see we were entering a clearing. A couple of hundred yards further on I could make out a deep cutting. It seemed like a steep-sided valley until we came closer and an old blue sign gave away its real identity: we were standing at the top of a cutting in which was situated the motorway once known as the M25.

Guards ordered us to stand at regular intervals along the embankment, armed with sticks. On the opposite bank of the motorway cutting I could make out a large crowd of several hundred people, emaciated and short in stature. These were refugees, I learned, who had been trying for some weeks to make it across the motorway into Hertfordshire. In spite of repeated attempts, few had been successful. Though the Duke's estate had been populated in the first place by refugees from London, in recent years he had sought to stop the flood. Too many, it was explained to me, were seeking work and nourishment on the Duke's land, and were putting undue strain on the resources available.

'Look at them!' said a sturdy young man beside me. 'Why can't the bastards stay where they belong? Coming and taking our food, our jobs! They don't want to give anything, they just take. And if you let one in, you can be sure there will be a hundred more round the corner waiting to join 'em.'

'Will the Duke not take any of these people?' I asked. 'The extra labour would surely be valuable.'

'What, urban people? Just look at them! Look at their chests; you can see their bones! There's no work in these people, just extra tummies to feed. They are all scroungers, Londoners. The Duke will have nothing to do with them, and quite right too. They can go back where they came from. London is their land and this is ours. It's well known that Londoners bring disease. There's been a cough going through the executive homes these past couple of weeks, and you know where it comes from? On the wind from London.'

We later got talking again. It transpired that he himself had come from London ten years earlier. But he did not see any contradiction between his origins and his attitude to Londoners now. 'It was different in those days,' he said. 'We came because we wanted to work, then. We respect the Duke. Would these people do that? Of course they wouldn't. You can tell just by looking at them. These people just want our food.'

The stand-off continued for an hour. The Duke's men waved and thumped their sticks. The Londoners just stared. A number of them began to drift away. Others were more persistent, calculating that sooner or later we would grow tired of maintaining the guard. It was impossible, they reckoned, for the Duke's men to guard the frontier constantly, and they would just wait their chance. Then, out of the blue, we heard shouting on our left flank. A small party of Londoners had broken their ranks and were racing down the embankment towards us. We were ordered to charge at them, which we did. We chased them and chased them, along the motorway, between the hulks of vehicles which remained there. Before long, we were half a mile away, well out of sight of the rest of the Duke's men. We had cornered a couple of youths who had run out of breath and were gasping by the side of an old van. I turned round and saw Bump standing behind me, and I had an idea. Quickly, I removed my orange vest and handed it to one of the youths, telling him it was his. Bewildered, it took him some moments to realise what was happening. The he quickly put on the vest and disappeared up the bank into Hertfordshire. Bump, too, gave his vest to one of the Londoners and within seconds we were clambering up the opposite bank of the motorway, free men – and in London. There was no time to look for the other members of my party, so off we went, just the two of us.

11

Great and terrible things are told of London now. The city is said to be in the hands of violent thugs and cheats who have reduced the majority to penury while they themselves have grown fat. The streets are rumoured to be lined with the bodies of unfortunates who were killed for their gold watches and chains. Whole districts are said to be inhabited only by rats. To walk the streets, some insist, is to tempt certain death from the debris of crumbling buildings. Folklore has Londoners grossly deformed by illness, bow-legged, lop-sided, their heads extended in all directions by gruesome tumours. There is said to be no food, save for other Londoners; cannibalism is said to be rife and practised by gangs who stalk neighbourhoods for young and succulent children.

It goes without saying that much of this is mischievous invention. The feudal lords of the shires have a great interest in spreading these tales in order to promote loyalty among their populations. London is the common enemy against which Progressive thought can unite. There being no alternative sources of information, the stories are easily believed. Few dare to venture to London to check them out, save for a handful of adventurers who have guessed at the possibilities for making fortunes in such a chaotic city.

To enter the city from the north, the London of myth and legend is far from obvious to the eye. You can walk for several miles over the remains of golf courses and through the backstreets of Barnet without encountering a soul. When eventually you do find people – the city grows steadily more populous as you approach the centre – they are to be found huddled at incredible densities, a dozen or more to a room. This is as much for safety as for warmth. Besides the house-dwellers there is a large drifting population of scavengers. When the two meet, the results can be horrific: Londoners speak of battles with knives and machetes, which have been known to end in rape and sacrifice. Londoners are organised, if that is the word, into 'communities'; huddles of people which in previous ages would have been known as tribes. They distinguish themselves in many ways. A hundred languages are spoken across the city, some of them of Asian and African origin though many of them dialects of nasal whines and glottal stops which have developed only in the past few years and seem to bear little relation to the spoken English from which they have been derived. The communities devise their own uniforms, manufactured from whatever salvaged clothing lies to hand. People paint their faces and wear jewellery to enhance their sense of belonging. Quite often, the credentials for membership of these communities are racial or religious in nature. But this is far from always the case. In some cases, a tribe has derived from a group of people who just happened to live in a particular place at a particular time. Near Totteridge, Bump and I got talking to a group of 50 people who were living in a pair of semi-detached houses, and asked how they came to be living together as they did. 'People in this street never used to speak in the old days,' the most elderly of their number told us. 'We didn't even know who was living next door to us. We were too involved with our own business. It was only when the refugees tried to set up an encampment at the end of the road that we got talking. We had a meeting. We started by writing letters to the authorities. When that didn't work, we organised watches, armed ourselves. How else were we to defend our property? Gradually, our houses fell into disrepair and we concentrated our efforts on maintaining just these two. My family came from Eastern Europe. I cannot remember the details, but they are unimportant. That is pre-history. Few people here have any idea of their distant origins. If you ask them where the come from they say "from this street". It is our identity.'

The community had become a very strong one, he told us. But in recent years it had come under threat because so many of the young men had left to seek a better life in Hertfordshire. 'Those of us who are left here are mostly elderly. It is a struggle for us to keep going, and we have all talked about leaving many times. But it is our land. There are some among us who believe God intended us to live in this street and so contrived to give it to us. You have to understand it is not something that we can easily give up.'

It was quite clear from the emaciated frames of the people we met that London is an impoverished place compared with the country around. There are many things unpleasant about life in the Progressive-run parts of England, but shortage of food is not generally one of them. In London, signs of hunger are everywhere. There is no cultivation, save for in the private yards of houses: attempts to grow food elsewhere invariably end in theft. People survive by scavenging nuts and berries and by trapping rabbits, foxes, badgers and any other animals which come to hand. At times of the year, this presents no problem. In high summer, people spend much of their time shinning up trees to steal fledglings from their nests. They block the holes of badger sets, them dig down and kill the animals with spades. But in winter, survival is much harder. Sometimes, Londoners are able to take advantage of traders who have come in from the country districts to sell food. But their visits are sporadic: they are increasingly discouraged by Progressive forces, and in any case there is no longer any great surplus of food in the immediate country districts around London. Too often, weeks of hunger give rise to battles between London's neighbouring communities, each accusing the other of straying upon their patch. As I say, these can end in appalling fighting.

There is a constant feeling in London that violence lies just around the corner. The people have adjusted to this. They are prepared for it when it comes, though they do not brood over it when it has taken place. They think it the most natural thing in the world to have to engage in fighting from time to time, and are less affected when they suffer losses than was the case with their industrial predecessors, who would fret over violence on their televisions though they seldom encountered it in real life. We passed a seemingly peaceful scene in Finchley: of women in headscarves, cooking; of men trapping rats for the pot and of children playing in the dust. It was only after we had been talking for some time that this community let slip that several of their number had been killed two days before in a fight over food. They had concealed their dead – pushed their bodies into long-disused drains rather than buried them properly – and what was there to do now other than to resume ordinary life?

Compared with the industrial age, people accept fate more easily these days because their lives are no longer blighted by high expectations. They do not plan for happiness, yet seem more prepared for it when it comes. On our way through North London, we kept coming across scenes of song and laughter. People paint, play instruments and dance. There is one common theme to all this activity: joy. There is no darkness in their culture. The nihilism of 50 years ago is entirely absent. 'It is quite obvious that life in the late industrial age was many times more violent than it is now,' said Bump. 'I have seen the film posters: there is nothing on them but death and destruction. There can only be one reason for this: that was people's common experience at the time.' I tried to dissuade Bump from this view, but without success.

For all the violence, it would not quite be true to say that London has descended into anarchy. Contrary to the position in the rest of the country, London is still in theory bound by the laws and regulations which existed 50 years ago. There is still a Government, there are still governmental departments, courts of law and a police force. It is just that their grip on the city is tenuous. This does not, however, prevent them from carrying on in a pedantic manner. On our first night in London, Bump and I broke into an empty house in Finchley to seek shelter. We had presumed it to be abandoned, but in the morning we were surprised by two police officers who arrested us and took us down to their police station. The owner of the house, it transpired, still lived opposite and had reported us. The officers were civil enough, but declined to hear us make our defence and insisted that the matter must be taken further. They then confessed that it was unlikely we would be charged owing to the backlog of cases. It was hopeless, he said: there were several years' worth of cases still to be considered. They bailed us and ordered us to report back to the police station in three weeks' time; a condition which we had no intention of fulfilling and they had little hope of enforcing.

'Cases of murder and robbery will come before your own, in theory,' one said. 'But your case will almost certainly be heard before the cases of cannibalism. That offence is widely tolerated. So long as the victim was scavenged rather than murdered, juries are reluctant to convict because they accept the argument than people are driven to desperate measures when they are hungry.' It is quite bizarre how people regularly fall foul of archaic and seemingly nonsensical regulations. People have sat down in the street and found themselves fined with obstructing the traffic; ignoring the obvious objection that there is no traffic to obstruct. People are still jailed for killing badgers, even though those once-endangered animals are in abundance and it is the people who are starving. There are people in cells whose only offence was to demolish a dangerously-leaning parapet on their homes. They have been convicted of changing a listed building without permission; it matters not to the prosecutors that survival is now clearly of more pressing importance than the aesthetic integrity of old buildings.

Yet for all the difficulties and hardships of life in London, there are greater freeedoms there than in the surrounding districts. The anti-industrial fervour of the countryside is not present in London. It is still possible to see the occasional vehicle in use; usually a moped or a lawnmower. There are people, too, who keep cars polished in hope of once again travelling in them, but these vehicles are not used because they are too complicated to repair and too refined to run on the fuel currently available. The source of the fuel which keeps mopeds and lawnmowers in operation came as a great surprise to me. I asked about it and was told that it came from the 'oil fields'. By the oil fields was meant Trafalgar Square and surrounding streets. Huge numbers of pigeons and seagulls have colonised these areas. Entrepreneurs risk death to scale buildings, clamber along ledges and snatch the birds from the ledges where they nest. The birds' flesh is eaten, then the feathers and bones are boiled up and oil skimmed from the top of the pan. No engine runs without problems on this fuel, but it is better than nothing.

Inadequate fuel is far from the only problem faced by people attempting to use mopeds. They can expect a swift visit from tax collectors and from the police, who will want to check the machine against several pages' worth of regulations. It is all but impossible for a vehicle these days to satisfy these rules, which have not been changed since the end of the industrial age. If subjected to an inspection, vehicle owners are invariably caught out by such things as loose wires or worn tyre treads. Vehicles are frequently confiscated – or stolen for the personal use of policemen.

The business of regulation still notionally employs tens of

thousands of Londoners. Their salaries are rarely paid, but their jobs have never formally been extinguished. Many hold on to their little positions out of pride, and continue with their paperwork even though their work has long become redundant. Peer through the windows of office buildings in Central London and quite often you can still see serious-minded elderly people writing and shuffling papers at their desks. They want to show off their brains, to which end they spend much of their time writing reports or memoranda which will never be read. They no longer take the risk of returning to homes in the suburbs at the end of the working day. Instead, they remain huddled in their offices, many of which have become closed to the outside world and are run along monastic lines. Courtyards are cultivated. Drinking water is obtained via gutters and downpipes; with the result that members of the community need venture outside only rarely.

The influence of the clerical classes is, however, declining. Younger people have little interest in office work and are instead turning to dangerous but more rewarding manual work. London is a much hungrier place than is the surrounding country, but it is more enterprising, too. Besides hunting and scavenging, there is a growing trade in food from overseas. The strictures against trade applied in Progressive-held parts of the country are not applied in London. Bump and I arrived at the Thames to find the waterside surprisingly busy. On the muddy expanses of tarmac by the river – many of the old roadways are now flooded at high tide – lay hundreds of small boats leaning on their keels. Their plastic hulls had gone yellow and their sails had been crudely repaired with tape. Pallet-loads of vegetables and sack-loads of grain were being unloaded from these boats: not enough, we learned, to feed everybody in London, but sufficient to provide the wealthy with a varied and sustaining diet. Some of the vegetables, we were told, had been imported via Calais, Antwerp and Rotterdam, though most had originated from much further East: Poland, Russia, Romania. In these countries, Progressive ideology is less established and the harvests are much greater than in England. The food is transported in convoys of wagons, or by railway, to the nearest port and put onto flotillas of yachts. The boats are frequently attacked and set alight, no stretch of the journey being as dangerous as the final 20 miles into London. The shores of the Thames estuary, we learned from seasoned mariners drinking spirits in riverside taverns, are riddled with bandits. Should you judge the wind wrongly, there is a danger of being driven to the shores of Essex or Kent, where gangs will ransack your vessel. Should the winds be too light, the bandits will swim out to you and overturn your boat. Many traders have been drowned in this way. The best chance of safety is in numbers: traders wait off Southend for several dozen other boats to arrive, then remain there, sometimes for days, for the winds and the tides to offer them a swift passage into London.

'Twice this happened to me,' we were told by Jan, a Russian sailor who was sitting by his boat at Blackfriars, basking in the sun while he awaited an ebb tide on which to sail for home. 'Thanks to a storm I was forced to land at Tilbury. Everybody says the same thing: nowhere are the bandits as vicious as at Tilbury. If you are lucky they will charge you a tariff and let you on your way. Otherwise, they capture you and charge you with dumping goods on the English markets. They take a quick look through your load and tell you that your food is diseased. Or they tell you that it is "genetic". They accuse you of trying to poison the people: though I have seen the thugs spirit away the food for their own use after having condemned it. They pour oil over your vessel and set light to it in the river. Then they beat you, accuse you of being a "globaliser" and chase you back into the river where, if you are lucky, you might get picked up by a passing vessel. Many, though, aren't so lucky. The sea's a graveyard at Tilbury. I have landed at ports all through the North Sea and through the Baltic, and I tell you there is none as dangerous as London.'

Then why, I asked Jan, did he come?

'The rewards, sir, the rewards. In no city do they shower you with such riches as in London. When the boats come in, Londoners bring down to the quayside every precious material you can imagine: gold, diamonds, ancient brooches and coins; Egyptian, Greek, Roman. You name it, it is in abundance in London. I am told there are vaults running for miles beneath the streets, brimming with these treasures. In Russia, food is plentiful, but we do not have the same artefacts.'

The whole world seemed to have tied up its boats along the Thames at Blackfriars. Thin and ragged mariners from mainland Europe were interspaced with fresh-cheeked adventurers from Eastern Africa who had brought cargoes of exotic dried fruits and seafood. These they sold at impromptu markets on the quayside, business being conducted in an excited patois. Many of these adventurers were making the return journey to Africa with a cargo of young London men who had been persuaded of the opportunities for personal enrichment in Dakar, Monrovia, Lagos and other cities of Eastern Africa. Sceptics tried to tell these wide-eyed hopefuls that they had been sold a false prospectus and that they would find themselves doing menial work and be unable to escape. 'I plead with you,' one father was saying to his son. 'It is easy to fall for these tales. But I tell you, life in Africa is no better than that in Buckinghamshire or Hertfordshire. You will be enslaved.' This cut little ice with the son, who shrugged his shoulders and boarded the boat, paying a fee of ancient coins to the tall black captain dressed in a richly-coloured coat. Other parents were more enthusiastic about sending their offspring abroad in search of a better life. Some of the children being loaded into the boats were barely in their teens. They gazed mournfully at their parents as they were waved off on a journey from which they knew there would be little chance of return.

We talked with the traders, anxious to know of the economic conditions in the countries whence they came. The interior of Africa, we were told, is a lost cause. Aids and warfare had once ravaged the population to the point of extinction. Few now venture further than a couple of miles inland. Yet the coastline is a different matter: many towns and villages have become independent states and are beginning to relearn the arts of agriculture and trade. 'We do not have the problems of over-population which afflict you in Europe,' one trader told us. 'It is so shocking to see the miles of hungry faces along the riverbanks in London. I was quite unprepared for desperation on this scale, and I will scarcely be believed when I return home.'

Sea travel, where allowed, is relatively easy these days; much more so than land travel. While their sails have needed patching, the old sailing yachts are still in good condition and run well. A couple of boats had even arrived from China laden with cargoes of rich spices. Their sailors marvelled at the backwardness of England. Were there no workshops in London, they wanted to know, to match those in China? They told us of the bangs and hisses of the streets of Beijing, where millions are employed turning out manufactures. In China, the mariners said, the industrial age was not considered to have ended, though it was accepted there had been some decline since their grandparents' day. The decline was considered to be temporary and might be put right by greater exploration of the world. The mariners told us they had made the journey to England not just to sell their spices, but in an attempt to locate the lost oil wells of the North Sea. They had been told of great fountains of oil spewing dozens of feet into the air, and imagined that they might catch it in buckets. I had to disabuse them of this belief, though I am not sure they accepted my word.

There was one group missing from the quayside: sailors from the Americas. We did, however, hear tales of Americans who had been washed up along the south coast, barely alive, their eyeballs bulging and their tongues blackened with disease. They had come, it was said, not to conduct trade or to seek a better life, but to prove to sceptical Americans that Europe existed, to which end they had hoped to gather some artefacts and sail for home. We were told, too, of a Londoner who had claimed to have set up a rudimentary wireless réceiver and to have received muffled signals which could only have come from the other side of the Atlantic. It is impossible to say whether these stories are true or whether they are fabrications, though it is clear that in common with the rest of the world the people in America possess a lower level of technology than was in use half a century ago, for otherwise we would hear much more from them.

12

It now fell to us to locate the Great Exhibition of Industrial Manufactures which had caused us to make our journey to London. Bump and I asked several people to point us in the direction of the event, and were surprised when nobody seemed to know to what we were referring. I repeated that we were searching for the Great Exhibition of Industrial Manufactures: an event, we had been promised, of great size and which it was said would be opened by the King. In some people this induced a flicker of recognition but they added regretfully they could not direct us there. It was extraordinary and alarming. We had been led to understand that this was an exhibition of international importance, and yet few in London seemed even to have heard of it.

Eventually, we had some luck. A boatman told us that he had ferried several people to Greenwich in recent days, and that they had mentioned an exhibition, though he could remember no further details. Having not the gold or silver for which he asked we set out to walk to Greenwich instead, facing immediately the problem of how we might cross the river. The bridges across the Thames these days are in dangerous condition and you take your chance in crossing them. London Bridge and Blackfriars Bridge have collapsed arches. Waterloo Bridge is a den of thieves. We had to pass upstream as far as Hungerford railway bridge before we could cross, and then only by clambering over rusty ironwork which we could not be sure would hold. There were thieves on the bridge and they pursued us, but they could not reach us before we were safely on the south side of the river.

The word 'exhibition' drew greater response on the south bank than it had on the north, though still we struggled to find anybody who had visited the event. 'Are you not curious?' I asked a young woman of around 20, called Lucy, whom we met in Southwark. She shrugged her shoulders as if to ask why should she want to see an exhibition. Had she travelled anywhere? She looked bewildered. 'I've not been out of this street,' she told us. 'Not in my whole life, except to go up to the river. Nobody I know goes across the river. And I daren't go south. My mother told me never to go beyond the Elephant and Castle. There's bad things down there, everyone knows it. You could bump into the Yardi.'

I asked her what she meant by this. 'The Yardi?' she replied. 'You have never heard of the Yardi? He is half-man, half monster, who lopes around and feeds on children and young adults. He has guns and daggers, and carries pills and white powders which can kill you in an instant. Surely everyone knows about the Yardi. No, whatever you do, you don't want to go beyond the Elephant and Castle.'

Lucy had not travelled far, but she had dreams. She carried next to her heart a photograph of a Jamaican beach, torn from the pages of an old holiday brochure, showing turquoise sea and palm-fringed beaches. This was the land, she told us, from where her people had come long ago, and it was her ambition one day to return. She had no idea of how to get to Jamaica; only that it lay 'over the sea'. Sometimes she went up to the river to smell the salty air and to watch the boats sailing down the Thames towards the open sea. In her imagination they were all going to Jamaica. 'One day I will go too, if only to die. It is paradise. Look, it says so below this photograph. Does that not say paradise? That's what my mother always told me it says.'

Most of Lucy's neighbours, it transpired, had frustrated ambitions to travel. They had all heard of exotic places across the sea. One man told us of a place called Efreeka, where the people feasted on mangoes all day long. Another spoke of Italy, where the people bathed in golden waters in a perpetual sunset, attended by virgins. There was an endless supply of wine and seafood. 'Look,' he said, also waving an old tourist brochure at me. 'This is where I will go when I go on holiday.' It was clear from his tone that he did not mean a holiday in the old sense of the word: he meant that this was where he was going to go when he died. In the uncomplicated religion of these people the words 'holiday' and 'paradise' had become one of the same thing.

No-one could blame the people of Southwark for having an exaggerated vision of old holiday destinations. They lived in houses grouped around the old tube station in a state of incredible poverty. Almost every Underground station these days has a community living close by, because the stations are synonymous with food. Their tubes and shafts have long since been breached by the river, becoming flooded twice a day. When the tide recedes, fish become trapped on the old steps and escalators, and are easily harvested by locals. There are also plentiful rats, which are captured in large nets by those prepared to risk their lives by descending into the tubes between tides. The rodents are then clubbed to death and fried over open fires. Fish and meat are the staples of the diet in Central London: the people can only stare at the fruit and vegetables landed on the Thames embankment and wonder at such luxury.

Presently, Bump and I came upon London Bridge railway station, where a surprise awaited us. A broadly-built crier with a peaked cap was standing outside bawling to passers-by: 'This way for the train service! Greenwich in half an hour.' What he said turned out to be true: there really was a train standing in the station waiting to carry passengers to Greenwich and providing a spectacle for dozens of people who wanted but could not afford to make the journey. The crier several times referred to the train as 'new'. This was clearly not the case: it had quite obviously been plundered from an old museum and coaxed back to some sort of life. But the wonder was that it was there at all. There were young children and adults who marvelled at the hissing machine, quite speechless. When it spat hot steam at them, some of the crowd withdrew in fear. When it emitted a high-pitched whistle, many turned and ran, starting a fracas which for a while seemed in danger of developing into a riot. People fell and screamed as the crowd was momentarily lost in a thick, swirling mist of smoke and steam.

A jet of steam was exhausted from the wheels and Bump fell to the ground, gasping for breath. 'The carbon dioxide!' he cried. 'I cannot breathe!' It was some time before I had managed to calm him down and to persuade him that he was not being suffocated. Gradually, he stopped panicking and his breathing returned to normal. He was nevertheless still unhappy. 'This is a crime against the environment!' he said. 'This machine is an instrument of global warming. It must be stopped, before the Earth is warmed and we are drowned by the rising sea!' I tried hard to persuade him that back in the industrial age there were millions of machines pumping foul gases into the air, and still we did not suffocate or drown. He did not believe this to be possible. His teachers, it emerged, had told him terrible things about machinery; even though they themselves had not seen a machine in action. At first, my efforts to explain that a single machine was incapable of destroying the Earth's climate and poisoning the people resulted in yet more snarling from Bump. Eventually, however, I managed to talk him around to taking a ride.

The train conductor accepted as our fare the few remaining items of worth in our pockets. We took our seats in the rear of the two coaches. In spite of the size of the crowd which had gathered to watch the train, few were travelling and we had the coach virtually to ourselves. A few minutes later, the train jolted into action, with a deafening squeak: so strange when you have become unused to the sound of machinery. As it did so, we were joined by a late middle-aged man in a tatty old suit but with an eager face. 'For Greenwich, are you?' he asked us. 'You're coming to the right place, you are. What do you know about Greenwich, then?' I told him that we knew about the exhibition, but that was about all; I had not been there for half a century. 'You've clearly done your research,' he went on. 'The exhibition is making a huge difference, and now with this train service, well, you can see the effect it is having. Greenwich in half an hour from Central London! Now, you're probably wondering where this is leading. And don't worry. I'm not trying to sell you anything. You're probably thinking that a property is the last thing you need. But I just want you to take a look at some houses which I have on my books.'

He then handed us a sheath of papers, each crudely scrawled with the drawing of a house, a few details about the number of rooms and a price writ large in bold pen. The noughts stretched right across the pages. It did not take close examination to establish that the pricing system was very simple: it was one billion pounds for a one-roomed house, two billion pounds for a two-roomed house, and so on.

'But how can you sell them?' I asked. 'London is full of abandoned houses which are free for the taking.'

'Not in Greenwich,' said the estate agent. 'Perhaps you can pick up an empty house in some parts of London, but in Greenwich you will find things very different. It is up-and-coming. If you want to buy in Greenwich, you shouldn't leave it too long. The prices have doubled in the week since the exhibition opened.'

'But I don't have a billion pounds,' I said.

'Don't worry. Nobody does. But you could borrow it. I can offer you some very good deals. So long as you can offer me a deposit in gold today, I can advance you the money straight away. No interest to pay until next year, by which time your home should be worth many times what it is today. Then you can trade up to a larger home. Everybody's doing it in Greenwich. And how fantastically wealthy they have become! There has not been an opportunity to make such riches in fifty years.'

Bump was mesmerized by the estate agent; I fancied he was even on the verge of being tempted. Before he could say anything, I quickly waved away the estate agent. That the man was little more than a common thief was clear later when we arrived in Greenwich to discover the houses there, as in all parts of London, to be in a poor state of repair, with missing roof tiles and shattered windows. Londoners have been caught out by such schemes before. The older among them still carry with them half-forgotten mortgage debts from half a century ago. Nobody can clear these debts, not even by selling the properties because the houses in which they live have little or no value. Those known to owe money are subjected to ridicule. Their doors are frequently daubed in red paint and their children are taunted in the street with the words 'Borrowers! Borrowers!' Occasionally, people will be visited in their homes by gangs calling themselves 'building societies'. The gangs will bundle the debtors onto the street and demand from them whatever they can muster. The secret to survival as a debtor is not to find some way of paying off the money, but to invest in good weapons. Everybody knows that in practice it matters little whether you are a million pounds in the red or a million pounds in the black: what determines whether you stay in your home or not is how good you are at fighting off thieves and bandits. If you do get thrown out by men from a 'building society', you do not have to raise money to buy another home; you merely have to go searching for another, empty one.

The train did not draw into Greenwich gracefully; it ploughed headlong into a heap of earth and sand which had been piled onto the track deliberately in order to arrest its motion. Passengers received an awkward jolt, with many being thrown from their seats. But most, thankfully, were unhurt. The organisers of the train service, it turned out, had mastered most of the engineering of a steam engine except for the brakes. We were assured, however, there was an engineer working on these and that they would be introduced the following week. Along with the other passengers, we brushed ourselves down and made our way to the station forecourt, where a fleet of taxis were waiting. These were in fact motor-cars, though each was drawn by a pack of 30 or so dogs, lashed to the front of the car with rope. The windscreen had been removed so that our driver could communicate with his dogs. A crack of the whip and we were on our way.

The driver agreed to take us to the exhibition, though could not help adding that he could see little purpose in the event. 'What are they hoping to achieve up there?' he asked. 'From what people tell me, they're trying to get machines working and the like! It's quaint, but what's the point? I mean, if I want to boil an egg I'm going to light a fire, heat up a pan of water and get on with it aren't I? I'm not going to mess around trying to make some electricity first. It's the same with cars. They're very useful, cars, when converted to dog-power. But you have to laugh at the thought of them in the old days trying to get hold of some petrol, then trying to get some sparks flying to start the engine. You think: by the time I'd gone through all that, I could have driven there with the dogs! They're just playing around up at that exhibition. They've got their heads buried in the sand, that's what.'

The exhibition hall became visible from some distance away: it was a large green and brown dome, which dominated the river side and sparkled in the sunlight. Only when we came closer did we realise that what gave it its sparkle was a thick coating of silvery bird-droppings, moss and general muck. In front of the dome, small clusters of people were milling about; you would not call them a crowd, but they gave the scene a degree of activity which we had not encountered in any other London suburb. As we approached, we saw that the area immediately outside the dome resembled something of a fairground. Fortune-tellers and weather-forecasters were plying a brisk trade. There were prostitutes soliciting, physicians dispensing potions and offering to read your blood-pressure. There were men who claimed to be able to tell the time – something they achieved by observing the angle of the sun. There was a bearded man who wanted to ask you a few questions and tell you your IQ, and a woman who wanted to measure your waist and tell you how long you would live. There were teachers who wanted to show you how to write or to add up, or who wanted to get out maps and globes and tell you where you were: on an island in the Atlantic. 'What strange novelties!' said one couple as they drifted aloofly by. 'Charlatans the lot!'

There were money-lenders standing by heaps of old banknotes: these, they tried to explain, were the currency accepted inside the exhibition and it was necessary to obtain them here. They would exchange these notes for jewellery or other items of worth. There were dancers, poets, musicians who strummed badly-tuned guitars and sang 20th century songs whose words had been corrupted into meaninglessness. Magicians and jugglers performed before small crowds. Painters scrawled over the canvas of the building: pictures, mostly, of matchstick figures scavenging for food in parts of London which they knew. Way above, attracting much attention, a stuntman ran up and down the roof. 'Health and Safety displays, twice daily,' shouted an accomplice. 'Roll up for the Health and Safety' display.' What he really meant, I soon worked out, was a dare-devil act, the term 'health and safety' having come to attain an ironic meaning.

Bump and I watched briefly, then headed inside the dome. The atmosphere was oppressively smoky. Many exhibition-goers were choking into handkerchiefs, while a small army of men in luminous yellow jackets were trying to blow the smoke away by flapping blankets towards the centre of the dome. It took a while for the air to clear sufficiently for us to see the origin of the smoke: it was a large fire which had been lit in the centre of the dome, fed by mountains of paper, wood and general rubbish which were being shovelled into the flames by mean in overalls. A large hole had been cut into the roof of the dome in an attempt to allow the smoke to leave, but the atmospheric conditions were clearly not favourable: much of the smoke was being trapped and was circulating within the building. Above the fire, an engineer had rigged up a boiler and some pipe work which carried hot water and steam throughout the building. Every so often, there was a hole in the pipework through which steam came gushing at great speed. To some of these openings, artisans had attached a number of rudimentary machines, among them a steam hammer, a power loom and an organ on which somebody was attempting to make a rendition of God Save the King in a series of out-of-tune, low-pitched hums. These machines were mostly failures. The power loom was not working at all, and was threatening to scald its frustrated inventor as he played around with its workings. The steam hammer, which consisted of little more than a lump of metal in a tube, was proving more functional, being put to use crushing small objects donated by visitors. One man marvelled as his hat was reduced to a pancake of steaming cloth. Another enjoyed the sight of a small clock being crushed to many pieces. One man donated a small coin for crushing. Bystanders were so impressed by the appearance of the flattened coin that they, too, emptied their pockets and offered coins for crushing, speculating that the squashed coins might gain in value. But nothing gained so much of a cheer as when somebody offered a small mouse to be despatched. When I ventured to the machine later, the artisan was to be heard shouting: 'Come and see a machine designed for the purpose of pest control!'

Most of the artisans were working from old books, adorned with richly-coloured diagrams but evidently lacking in the detail required to make a functioning device. 'It is a farce!' said Bump. 'The industrial age was a cruel deception. This proves it. Much of the machinery of the industrial age was myth. I know there were cars, but they can seldom have travelled much faster than walking pace. There were never aeroplanes. They are impossible. There were drawings of them, but they were dreams. Just look: the only machine which the organisers of this exhibition has been able to reproduce is an instrument of oppression: an execution machine!'

The smoke cleared to reveal a long table alongside which were standing a couple of dozen people, busily working with their hands. We ventured closer to find that they were engaged in the business of bottling shrimps which had been caught in the Thames. 'Convenience foods, as good as the supermarkets used to make them,' explained a heavily-bearded man who introduced himself as the overseer. 'We have proved that by adopting an industrial method of production we can increase the daily output of shrimps tenfold. Each person, you see, sticks to his own specialised task, at which he becomes very good, very quickly. One will salt the shrimps, another will pour them into the bottles and another will seal the bottles. Out on the river, others are employed catching these shrimps with large nets. The process of preservation has had a dramatic effect on the food supply. Before we began, there were great shortages of seafood during the winter months. Now, Greenwich is able to enjoy shrimps all year round, and we are even beginning to export some of our product.' He then showed us huge piles of boxes of potted shrimps due for carriage to Antwerp and Rotterdam.

'This must be stopped!' said Bump, quite shocked at what he was witnessing. 'It is an unsustainable activity! The shrimps will be driven to extinction. By putting them into plastic bottles you are turning the shrimps into junk food. People who eat them will be struck down with strokes of the brain. And your workers, their hands will be reduced to numbness by the repetitive activity you are forcing upon them. They will go mad and spend years of idleness. It is true. I have learned these things from my teachers.'

The overseer was taken aback by this attack on his business. 'But they are the finest shrimps,' he said. 'People have been eating them for many weeks without ill-effect. Our workers are quite happy with their work. If you like, I will show you the waters where they are caught and you can see for yourself the abundance of shrimps. Our production is already running at one barrel a day, but there is scope for much more once we begin to penetrate the export market. I advise you to invest. This is the ideal time to buy our shares. I have sent a delegation to Belgium, and once we begin to sell our shrimps there, well, the potential for expansion is virtually limitless.'

'But you will ruin people's diets,' said Bump. 'They will become fat and enfeebled, just like the people in the industrial age. You will end up killing people just in order to enrich yourself. You are profiteering. You must not be allowed to get away with it.'

The overseer would have nothing more to do with Bump, though he did point us in the direction of what he called the stock market, where we would be able to buy shares in his business. We crossed the floor to find a small ring of tables, upon which men were standing, bawling to passers-by: 'Get your shares here! Thames shrimp fisheries: twenty seven pounds, up from twenty five this morning. Greenwich Railway: Thirty pounds.' Most exhibition-goers were clearly puzzled by the exercise, though a small amount of business was being done. A few older people were parting with valuables and taking away hand-written share certificates. 'It's been a year of difficult trading conditions,' one stockbroker told us when I enquired as to who was buying these shares. 'But we are confident that conditions are now right for a sustained recovery. There are good prospects for earnings growth, particularly in recovery stocks. We advise a focus on growth stocks in the UK sector this year.' It was clear from his tone that he had little idea what he was talking about: when I looked closely I could see that he was simply repeating words he had learned from some financial brochure published many years before. Other salesmen were little more convincing. There was much excited talk about a 'coal rush' in Derbyshire. The old mines were being reopened, we were told, and found still to contain large quantities of coal. A new discovery had been made. 'Of course, the power stations have been closed for many years,' one stockbroker explained to me. 'But we have found that it is possible to burn coal in your own home. This cuts out the need for a power station, making the whole business so much more efficient. It is a wonder nobody thought of it in the industrial age.'

Occasionally, people would go much further than simply lighting coal fires: they would get steam engines going. This, however, was a dangerous thing to do. The engines were being suppressed by Progressive forces. It was said that in one town, a man caught operating a steam engine had been held over his engine and boiled alive. Yet such was the determination among the steam engine-owners to revive their machines that such threats would not deter them.

'Go to Derbyshire, young man!' called a stoutly-built man with long white hair, who grabbed Bump by the shoulder and waved a bag full of small black stones in the other hand. 'That's where the money's to be made: in the coal mines. There's a lad not much older than you whom I sent up to Derbyshire a few months back, and he's a powerful man now. I'm launching a venture. You won't believe what I've found: an entire hill made of coal! You scrape away the soil and it is everywhere: fat lumps of coal. And people thought the oil and coal had all gone! You wonder why they never found this coal back in the industrial age. But truth was, they were looking in the wrong place: the wrong side of the road. Think of the riches when we get to sell it to the shivering masses! I'm not telling you exactly where this coal is, of course, unless you sign up. But let me just tell you it's a place called Slag Hill. Buy shares in the Slag Hill coal mine! Subscribe today, or the chance will be gone for good.'

He was interrupted by a stockbroker in a suit so threadbare that his knees shone through. The stockbroker tugged on Bump's sleeves. 'But there are much better mines than this. Out in Essex there has been opened a mine which has much greater treasures. The company has dug down and found bathtubs, bicycles, items of clothing: all perfectly formed! They have been taken out, the earth cleaned from them and put to use. And so far the miners have only been a few yards into the hill. Yet the hill goes on for half a mile! What treasures there must still be hidden there, what wonders! People once believed these sorts of things were manufactured by man, but here they are, spewing out of the virgin earth! It is a miracle. This is what happened in the industrial age: men came across these great seams of perfectly-formed industrial goods. Now that we have succeeded in finding further seams, industrial civilisation will be back on its feet in a whisker. I warn you sir, don't let this opportunity go. There is fabulous wealth in this venture such as has never before been seen on Earth.'

Bump worked himself loose from the man's grip quite angrily. 'I will have nothing to do with it. Have you not been taught about the diseases which struck those who worked down the mines? They choked to death on their own sputum, so foul was the air they were forced to breathe. The Earth was not made to be treated in this way. If you disturb the Earth you will die horribly, and you will deserve it.'

Just then, our attention was taken by a message delivered by a man with a megaphone standing on a little stage. The aircraft demonstration was about to begin. We looked up and saw, as far as we could through the smoke, that a small glider and a pilot had been hauled to the roof of the dome via a system of ropes. 'Ladies and gentlemen,' came the announcer's voice. 'Will you please witness the return of the aeroplane! Watch and see for yourself how the ancient art of flying has been rediscovered. Now that the principles have been proven once more, we believe is only a matter of months before we will be able to fly again across the

Atlantic Ocean. Once you have witnessed this flight, there will be an opportunity to buy tickets for the resumption of airline services to America.'

We watched a little anxiously as the small glider – made from a wooden frame covered with paper – was released from its berth high up on the roof. It circled round the centre of the building several times, passing in and out of the smoke, before landing on a place which had been cleared as a runway. It juddered and scratched its way to an uncomfortable rest to one side of the dome. When it stopped, there was silence for a moment, before the pilot clambered from his cockpit and raised his arms in triumph. A few groups of mostly elderly onlookers broke out in spontaneous cheering. There was, however, some dissatisfaction. A number of people complained that the smoke had prevented them seeing the flight properly. After some negotiation, the man with the megaphone rose to make a further announcement: because of the importance of this occasion, and the interest which was being taken in it, it had been agreed that the fire in the centre of the dome would be extinguished for a while in order for a second flight to be made in more visible conditions.

While the fire was being put out, Bump and I were accosted by a woman carrying a clipboard. 'Please tell me your names,' she said. 'And tell me where you have come from.' Given that travellers can put themselves at great risk by revealing themselves to be outsiders, I hesitated. Why did she require this information? 'We are doing a survey,' said the woman. 'We are building up a database.' To what purpose, I asked? 'In order to study the population. We cannot hope to reconstruct industrial civilisation without a database. We are starting in London, and intend to cover the entire country by next year. It will tell us everything about everybody.'

I said that I did not mind her asking her questions, and she began to read from her papers: 'What weight are you? What height are you? How much do you earn a year: a. under £15,000;

b £15,000 to £25,000; c £25,000 to £40,000; d £40,000 to £60,000; e over £60,000? If you could, would you be interested in going on holiday in Cyprus?' At that point, I suggested she should stop. Plainly, she was merely reading from a market research questionnaire of many years before. It mattered to her not one bit that the questions no longer meant anything to anyone: they had been extracted from the hallowed archives of the industrial age and so far as she was concerned that made them of great value.

There were several dozen people working on this database. They were crouched over sheets of paper, transcribing from notebooks in great detail. I looked to see that the database contained long lists of names, scored underneath which were the collected replies to long lists of multiple choice questions. What, I asked, was the purpose of this survey and to what use would the information be put?. 'We have discovered, for example that very few people will be going to Cyprus on holiday this year, which tells us that there would be little point in reinstating an airline service there. We have discovered, too, that more people are looking for a sports utility vehicle than are looking for a hatchback. This is of course all vital information to aid the reconstruction of the industrial system.' I bothered her no more, and she returned studiously to her work.

Shortly, the man with the megaphone climbed onto his stage once more and announced that there would be another flight of the aeroplane. The visibility was now better and everybody could see as the glider was winched up to the ceiling with ropes and released. Expectations were high, but this time the plane seemed to descend much faster and with much less control. Without managing to execute a single turn, it struck a pillar and plunged to the ground, striking several exhibition-goers. There was a moment of confusion before an eruption of gasps and cries of horror. Some rushed over to help the injured and dead, at least one of whom had been decapitated. Others dashed for the doors, fearing the building might fall. Somebody shouted 'Terrorist attack! This is how the terrorists used to attack; I have read about it. Evacuate the building at once!' Others sniffed and said that they had been quite sure the exercise would come to grief and nobody would ever get them up into an aeroplane at any price. A couple walked with great purpose to the stand where they had just bought their airline tickets to America and demanded their money back, protesting bitterly when they found nobody there. An elderly man grabbed everybody he could and tried to lecture them on 'thermals'. 'It was the fire,' he said. 'They needed the heat, for the thermals. That's why the plane crashed: an absence of thermals. Please believe me: I was once a pilot.' He was told by young man to keep quiet: 'Shut up, you! There are too many people here with their crackpot theories. It is thanks to people like you that these accidents happen.'

It took the man with the megaphone some time to attempt to take control of the situation. There was clearly the threat of a riot. He thought quickly and announced to the hall: 'Please be calm. This situation is under control. We will find out the cause at the public inquiry.'

What, I asked a bearded fellow beside me, was meant by this? 'The public inquiry?' he said. 'Have you not heard of the public inquiry into the causes of the decline and fall of industrial civilisation? It has been going on for 17 years.' Many, he added, had forgotten the existence of the inquiry, but since the exhibition opened it had begun to attract large crowds. The Royal Courts of Justice were now unable to cope, and so as of tomorrow the inquiry was to be relocated to the exhibition hall itself.

At dusk, the exhibition closed and everybody was asked to leave the premises. Bump and I slept huddled against the outer skin of the tent. Fortunately, it was a calm night and there were many others sleeping alongside us to help keep us warm. Our hunger was moderated by a distribution of soup, courtesy of the organisers of the exhibition. 'They say that in the old days there was soup distributed all over London, every night,' said a man next to us who had bedded down with his wife. 'Nobody went hungry, there was so much soup. Can you imagine that? The luxury! The efficiency! What a comfortable time it must have been to be alive!'

13

In the morning we returned to the exhibition hall to see a large increase in the number of visitors. It was clear what was the main attraction: the public inquiry, which was being set up in the centre of the dome. Scores of boxes stuffed with papers were brought in, and two hundred or more seats were arranged around the centre of the hall. But they were insufficient: there were crowds as far as one could see, fanning themselves with bits of paper to gain relief from the heat of the morning. When all were assembled, a team of inquisitors in black gowns entered with great solemnity and took their seats at a long table. As they did so, the chatter ceased and there was silence save for the hiss of various steam devices in the background.

'Can I call Mrs Bathsheba Bones to finish her testimony from yesterday?' asked the chief inquisitor. And Mrs Bones hobbled to the witness stand with the aid of two sticks.

'As I was saying when you closed down proceedings last night, your lordship, the miseries of the current age can all be put down to radiation from televisions and mobile phones. It slowly cooked our brains. It was meant to, wasn't it: these machines were designed to turn us into zombies. It was a plot on the part of the industrialists: they wanted us stupid so then they could play around with us, like we were their toys. It was a good job that we noticed what was being done to us before our brains were finished off for good. I was one of the victims. I have been left with this permanent fizzing inside my head. It's there from when I get up in the morning to when I go to bed at night. Fizz, fizz, fizz, all day long. It's all that radiation still buzzing around inside me.'

Mrs Bones went on for some time about her condition, until eventually she was interrupted by the inquisitors, who pointed out that she was repeating herself. They suggested that she might quickly bring her evidence to a conclusion. She was replaced at the witness stand by a succession of people who had similar complaints to make. 'My problems were caused by my having to sit down all day,' said one who was bandaged from head to toe; a condition in which he said he had been confined for the past 20 years. 'That was the biggest cruelty of the industrial age. We are supposed to be creatures of action, but we were forced into unnatural sloth. Millions were killed by the contortions into which they were forced at their desks or at the wheels of their cars. Their blood could not circulate and their backs caved in, reducing them to a pitiful condition. And don't let anyone tell you it didn't happen. There are pictures of hundreds of workers undergoing such torture in those killing fields which were once called "offices". The worst of it was that many of the victims were smiling. So subtle was this form of execution that they did not realise what was being done to them. What evil Man is capable of inflicting on his fellow Man! What utter misery was this episode of history!'

'It wasn't just the contorted positions which we were forced to adopt,' complained a wheezing woman who had to stop every so often for a deep breath. 'We were robbed of our sleep. We were kept awake, deliberately and maliciously, by noises repeated 24 hours a day. Our shops, streets and homes were bombarded with great bangs and thumpings which mashed the insides of our bodies to a hopeless pulp. This was done to destroy us. The musicians who did this to us were evil. How I shudder with rage to think what they did to me! The noise was addictive. We could not stop ourselves listening to it – at an ever-increasing volume until it pulverised our ear-drums. Look at me now: I am a wreck. The music made my nerves vibrate to the point at which they split. It is called fraying of the nerves. It was very common in those days, and is still common among older people. If I look at my hands very carefully in the right conditions of light, I can see them, these frayed nerve endings. Look at the state of them! It was evil of the musicians to do this to me. For this, I can never forgive.'

The next witness was crying as she took the stand. In the five minutes she was there she never once looked up, but carried on speaking until the chief inquisitor intervened and suggested that she should put herself under no more punishment. 'I am truly sorry for what I did,' she sobbed. 'But I was only a young girl and my defence is that I knew no better. I worked in a pharmaceutical factory, making vitamin pills. I cannot account now for why I did such a thing, but I did. Why? Why? I keep asking myself that, but I don't suppose I shall ever know the answer. The only thing I can say is that there was pressure on me to do what I did. It was hard to survive in those days unless you signed up to serve the industrial system in some way. But how can I make these excuses in view of the lives I ruined? These pills were designed to turn people into mutant beings. It was supposed to give them perfect hair, perfect teeth, perfect fingernails. The people fell for this, they did. And they ended up dying from terrible cancers as a result. What did it do to their minds? Turned them into idiots, that's what. And do you know what? My bosses knew this all along. I used to hear them plotting in the boardroom: how could they make people buy more and more of their pills? I know how they did: they put substances in those pills that made you want more and more. Those pills hooked you until you no longer had a mind of your own. I'm sure of it. But why did I aid this terrible industry? I will never forgive myself.'

There followed several more confessionals before the inquisitors called a dishevelled figure who bit his fingernails constantly. He had a quite different tale to tell. He had been an industrialist himself, he said. 'These people who now moan about these murderous industrial goods, I bet they couldn't buy them quick enough,' he said. 'They are nothing but hypocrites! They have been swept along by this anti-industrial fervour for no reason other than that it is fashionable. They are ungrateful beyond belief. I am proud to call myself an industrialist. I did everything I could to make the world a richer place, but at every turn I was thwarted by the kind of parasites we have heard from this morning. Think of all the great and wonderful things the industrial age gave us: the cars, the aeroplanes, the space rockets, the anti-static trouser conductors – let's not forget them. It's easy – oh, terribly easy – to think that the whole population was beavering away making these things. But the fact is they weren't. It was a tiny number of us who made the goods and maintained them. The rest were just parasites, who consumed everything we made and now have the gall to complain about it.'

'What was the nature of your business?' asked the chief inquisitor.

'I invented and manufactured the anti-static trouser conductor.'

There was mocking laughter from some sections of the audience.

'And what was an anti-static trouser conductor?' asked the chief inquisitor.

'It doesn't happen so much now, maybe because people don't drive round in cars any more. But in the old days, people often used to complain about getting electric shocks when they sat down, especially getting in and out of cars. It was potentially fatal, because the sparks could ignite the petrol and consume the entire vehicle in conflagration. By attaching a small strip of conductive material to the hems of their trousers, you could safely discharge the static electricity and prevent any ill-effects.'

By this point, the industrialist was unable to continue: his voice had been drowned out by mocking laughter from the crowd. 'Is this normal for the inquiry, what we have heard this morning?' I asked a spectator sitting next to me. He said that it was. 'I quite despair,' he went on. 'We have people like this every day. They are quite unable to see beyond their own misfortunes. They are of little help in trying to get to the bottom of this matter.'

The next witness then took to the stand: an elderly man with a shock of long white hair trailing halfway down his back. 'Fear,' he said. 'It was fear that did for the industrial system. That's the reason why we are so pitifully poor compared with our grandparents. In the last years of the industrial age I was a young man just embarked on a career in the oil industry. It was an industry which had made great fortunes for the people who had entered it years before, but not for me. Within a few months I was a pauper. Do you know what people say when I tell them this? They say that it is all my fault and I must have known that the oil was going to run out. It is hard to know what to say to these fools. I was in a position to know, and I tell you it is a falsehood that the oil ran out. There is plenty of oil left underground. I have seen the charts, and I could tell you where it is. I could tell you how deep you have to dig and the quality of the oil you could expect to find there.'

The inquisitors were becoming increasingly puzzled. 'Then how do you account for the fact that oil vanished from the economy?' one asked.

'The oil reserves were not exhausted; it is just that the price went up and the people panicked. They filled their tanks and hoarded oil in their homes. The demand was such that the price rose further, making people hoard all the more. The panic was exploited by racketeers, and the moment was seized by the terrorists, or environmentalists as they used to be known at the time. They stormed the petrol stations, sabotaged the tanks, blockaded the oil refineries, set light to tankers. It was astonishing how quickly the machinery of the oil industry was destroyed.'

'You say that you know where there is oil to be found,' said the chief inquisitor. 'Would you be able to lead a small team from the inquiry and prove your assertion.'

'That would be difficult,' said the former engineer.

'Why?'

'It would take more than one man to extract the oil. It was a hugely complex operation, involving many people, and tools which we no longer have.'

There was much jeering at these words, a lot of it from a small crowd of men in smocks who had recently entered the hall. 'Does this man take us for idiots?' asked one toothless young fellow. 'How are we expected to believe him, when he cannot even lead us to the oil he claims to be there?' The former engineer attempted to repeat his point. But he was quickly driven from the witness stand by onlookers stamping their feet.

Further witnesses came to give evidence. A young woman with bedraggled hair went into great detail about the scenes of inebriation which characterised the cities of the late industrial age: scenes which it was obvious from her age she can never have witnessed. 'It was barely possible to move for drunks and drug addicts,' she said. 'People were forced to intoxicate themselves. This is what did for the industrial age. The workers of 50 years ago could barely keep on their feet. The streets were encrusted with sputum, and the gutters flowed with blood from fights between these immoral people. It is little wonder that these people left behind little of intelligibility. The pages and pages of nonsense which are frequently produced: these were the work of inebriates whose minds had been destroyed! They supped with the devil and it was little wonder that they ended up writing the language of the devil.' She had, she said, some literature to prove what she meant; with which she produced pages upon pages of differential equations, ripped from a mathematical text book.

An elderly lady in a purple headscarf stepped up to tell us that this analysis was totally wrong: the problem was that the drugs had run out. 'For some reason, the supplies of cocaine could not be sustained,' she said. 'The same with the coffee, the crack and the speed. It was this failure which resulted in the enfeeblement of the human body. How could people be expected to continue to work without these essentials? People used to perform wonders when they had the sustenance to do so. But just look at them now: they sleep half the time; the rest of the time they are bumbling about, at half the speed we used to go about our business. What happened to the work ethic? It disappeared, that's what; vanished with the supply of drugs. One thing's for sure: industrial society won't be coming back until we've solved the drugs supply problem.' She received nods of agreement. But she was then denounced by a gaunt youth in a boiler suit. 'Oh, it wasn't young people who were enfeebled,' he said. 'Just look at the elderly: you are the ones who hobble about. Your back is nearly bent double and you are as unstable on your legs as a new born chick. What more proof do we need that the people of the industrial age were the enfeebled ones? Feeble mind, feeble body; it's all the same. You have no strength, no toughness, you leftovers from the industrial age. How often do you see an industrial person sobbing into a rag and muttering to himself how unfair everything is? Time and time again, that's what. And no wonder: self-pity was bred into you industrial people from the day you were born. You don't want to face up to life, you just want to sit down and blame everyone else for your misfortunes. What a disgraceful age it was which produced such people!' For this, the boy received many cheers.

A bald-headed fellow then stood up to say how much he agreed. It was nonsense that industrial-age people were responsible for the industrial goods which they were credited with making. 'It is downright nonsense. It is well known that the machines with which they shared the Earth were not made of Man. Men used them but they did not create them. They couldn't have done. What man could have created an aeroplane many hundreds of feet long? He could never have lifted the pieces into place. They were created by the gods, these things. I tell you, it is obvious. Think of the computers: I have never yet met a man who could satisfactorily explain to me how those devices used to work. Nothing we have heard in this inquiry so far has recognised that. We've had witnesses trying to come up with some explanation as to how mankind lost his nerve and his will to create. And yet it is quite obvious that man never created anything in the first place. This is the question we should be addressing: why is it that the gods, who gave us these things, suddenly decided to take them from us? I don't know the answer to this question, I'm afraid, but I do know that this inquiry will be a waste of time until we start asking it.'

The chief inquisitor asked him whether he had any evidence for his assertion that machines were the work of the gods. 'Of course I do,' he replied. 'They were put on the Earth in the year 1851, when men were still savages. They were shown off by the gods in a glass temple, where they were discovered by Man. It is all in the books. Look them up! There is a catalogue, and tales of wonderment at what men found there in the temple.'

He received a polite response; there were many in the building, it turned out, who shared his belief, and who went about proudly calling themselves Creationists. 'Why did the machines fall out with Man?' began the next witness. 'Why, that is obvious. It was the way they were treated. They were shown contempt. People took them for granted, and began to smash them up when they refused to work. You don't believe me? I saw it every day: people kicking their computers because they refused to co-operate. No wonder the machines began to strike back. No wonder the aeroplanes used to crash and factories used to explode. It was punishment for the follies of Man. It served us right. Our present wretched condition is as much as we deserve.'

There were nods of agreement from the growing crowd of smock-wearers, but all changed when the next witness took the stand: a old man who squinted through his spectacles. There are not many spectacle-wearers these days, and those who do wear them draw a dangerous degree of attention to themselves: glasses are the mark of an industrialist. The spectacle-wearer's evidence was soon drowned out by jeering, and before long he was driven from the witness stand. He sat down amid a torrent of abuse. 'This is an outrage!' shouted one man at the back of the hall. 'It is a slander on us all. Take him away!' The chief inquisitor appealed for calm, but many others managed to add to the abuse before order was restored and a stocky fellow in wellington boots and a smock fashioned from an old shell suit took the stand. 'There is one reason for the decline of conditions in this country and one reason alone,' he bawled above the racket. 'The Chinese! It was the Chinese. They took our jobs. They destroyed us. They settled among us and they finished us. Stole our country, they did. There were hard-working men on these shores before the Chinese arrived. It's all the work of the Chinese! They sent to us television sets and all manner of gadgetry which foolishly we bought. We did not know at the time that it was all programmed to hypnotise us. The televisions stole our personalities, made idiots of us. This was an evil act, and we must get back!' The inquisitor got it out of the fellow that he used to work in a factory whose work had been taken over by a factory in China, but this admission did nothing to stop him, and he ranted on for several minutes more. The proceedings then steadily degenerated as various members of the audience launched attacks on those they believed to be responsible for the decline of industrial civilisation. 'The muslims!' said a ruddy-faced woman with sweat dripping down her chin. 'They took our money. They took over our streets, our schools. They stopped us breeding. They did, I tell you. I can speak from experience. The muslims, they bred like farm animals, but they put something in the water which stopped us English breeding. Why otherwise did I never have a child?' Another shouted: 'The jews fooled us! They enticed us into their banks, then stole our pensions! They used to money to build grand villas in Palestine. I have seen the pictures! They did this with our money, and left us destitute.' Then came a cry from the side of the room: 'The jews were just scapegoats. It was the spectacle-wearers who were the evil ones. I tell you, just look at the photographs left over from the industrial age: look at the people who ran the banks, the ministeries, the businesses: so many of them wore spectacles that it cannot be a coincidence! They crept into all the positions of power: just count them! They destroyed us, these people.' 'These *people*?' cried another. 'You are calling spectacle-wearers human? It is now established beyond doubt that they were half man, half machine. Their eyes and their brains of these robots were installed by the engineers, in an experiment which went horribly wrong. The idea was that these machines would do all the hard work for us, while we would enjoy leisure time. But what happened was that their wiring proved to be faulty, and they developed free will. And you can guess what they did with this free will, can't you? They decided to suppress us. So that's what they did. And they are not entirely gone even now: that spectacle-wearer down there, he should be captured and caged!'

The spectacle-wearer turned puce with fright, lowered his head and tore off his glasses as others bayed at him. He may well have been captured had the mood in the hall not turned again. 'What about the paedophiles?' shouted a woman in a thick shawl. 'They ate our children. You just tell me they didn't. I've seen the bones! Piles of bones down where the paedophiles live. And they're still out there, feasting on human flesh. They grab children in the street. I've known it happen.' 'What about the dark people?' asked another. 'It was they who drove the trains; the trains which carried so many people to their deaths in horrible collisions, and sliced them in half on the railway tracks. Dark people, that's who it is: tribes of dark people. I warn you, don't let your children out. The dark people will get them.' 'This is wrong,' said a dark woman from the back of the room. 'The people whom you talk

about were the victims. It was the Elthamites who ruined the city
– and still do. They came on the trains, drunk on beer, and raped
the women and smashed the windows of our businesses. They
fought with knives. There is no reason to what they do. They are
animals, these people. I know, because my family were killed in
Lewisham by a mob of Elthamites.'

By now, the inquiry was quite out of control. Several dozen
people were standing up, trying to speak at once. There were fist-
fights. The inquisitors were quite unprepared, and had to force an
adjournment before order could be restored. During the enforced
break, Bump and I wandered through the exhibits. There was still
much to see. In a far corner, a giggling young couple were
spinning round and round on swivel chairs which clearly had been
salvaged from some office and crudely patched up with any
material that came to hand. 'It's amazing what they're doing for us
these days,' said some onlookers in wonderment. 'Such incredible
inventions!' In another place, two exhibitioners standing 20 yards
apart were talking to each other via a pair of telephone handsets,
connected via a long piece of string. They struggled to hear each
other, but nevertheless those who stood around watching the
spectacle were impressed. 'We are close to recreating the
telephone,' one of the exhibitioners then explained to the
gathered crowd. 'But there are still some problems we cannot as
yet seem to solve. There is clear evidence that people were able to
have conversations with each other not just in adjoining rooms
but from one end of the country to the other. How did they do so
without the string getting snagged? And we have come to the
conclusion that part of the skill in conducting a telephone
conversation lies in reading the lips of the person at the other end
of the line. How did they do this when the person whom you are
speaking to is out of sight? It is quite a mystery to us at present.
But of course it will be resolved. We have people working on it.'

An elderly, emaciated man who was watching burst into
laughter. 'You have not the first idea!' he bawled. 'I used to be a

telephone engineer and I tell you, you have little understanding. I would love to be able to help you. To start at the beginning, does the term "local area network" mean anything to you?'

The fellow was stared at as if he were a madman. 'Off with you!' shouted one onlooker. 'We have seen so many old people here fantasising about things they think they used to do. They seem to think they know everything, these old ones.'

The atmosphere in the hall was changing. Whereas a day earlier the exhibition-goers had been inquisitive and relaxed, now there were huddles of people talking in hushed tones behind pillars. The men in smocks who had been attending the public inquiry were to be found parading around the exhibits with stern faces and exchanging whispers. Bump and I were taken aback when we revisited the bottled shrimp production line to find three of the men in smocks haranguing the foreman. We could only hear snatches of the conversation, but it seemed that shards of glass had been found in one of the jars, and one consumer had been taken ill with food poisoning. 'You are committing an act of profit,' we heard one of the men in smocks say. 'We thought this practice had been stamped out years ago. It will not be tolerated.'

A short distance away, a crowd had gathered to watch a man who was screaming on the ground in pain. It turned out that he had been attacked – mortally as it later turned out – by thugs who had caught him writing out a flow diagram. He had been attempting to explain to people the principle of the computer and how that device might be resurrected. But the thugs had seen what he was writing and challenged him. 'That is the language of the devil!' they had declared before stabbing him several times.

At this point, Bump and I could easily have escaped. It would have been nothing for us to slip out of a side door and make our way from the exhibition. It was my undoing that we were to run into some of the organisers of the exhibition, who correctly identified me. 'Professor Gonne?' asked a bearded figure, tugging on my arm. I acknowledged that this was who I was and he went on: 'We have been expecting you for some days. It is an honour that you have come. Your scholarship is reputed to be among the finest in the land. I am so sorry that you come at a time when the proceedings should be disrupted in this fashion. It seems there is a large party from Essex with us today, who have little idea of the standards of behaviour expected at a public inquiry. But we are, of course, bringing matters under control. You would, I imagine, be willing to give evidence to the public inquiry?'

Feebly, I agreed. There was not even much time for preparation before the inquiry recommenced and I was led to the witness stand.

14

The chief inquisitor leaned across and said: 'I have your name down as Professor Matthew Gonne, Master of Trinity College, Cambridge. Is that correct?'

I confirmed that it was.

The inquisitor went on: 'Would you please present any information to this inquiry that you consider to be relevant to the decline of industrial civilisation.'

'It is a job to know where to begin, but let me say this. For the latter part of the industrial age there was great fear that civilisation would end with a bomb. This was a perfectly reasonable fear: for the last 70 years or so of industrial civilisation sufficient weaponry existed for the destruction of all life on Earth. Moreover, there were several occasions on which nuclear war appeared to be on the brink of occurring. The prospect of nuclear devastation was an unpleasant fact to have to live with, and one which impinged upon our collective consciousness in many ways. Scenarios were imagined in which a few wretches would be left to fend for themselves in a horribly burned landscape, nearly all life irradiated out of existence. We imagined blast waves, mushroom clouds, stygian fires smouldering for years afterwards.

'The bomb, when it came, was quite different. It did not lay waste to any landscape. It did not result in any injury, directly. Rather it exploded deep inside the world's computers. It was designed not to destroy life but to strike at the finances of every man, woman and child in the world. This it achieved with the utmost efficiency. Had it been less successful we would by now know the names of the perpetrators. We would know why they did it and we would know exactly how they did it. Yet such was the chaos they caused that there is no possibility they will ever be traced. But let me surmise this: the attack cannot have been the work of one or two people. It must have been the work of dozens, perhaps even hundreds, involving many years of planning. It is possible that they did what they did for political ends. Or possibly they did it simply because they realised it could be done. Perhaps they horribly underestimated the havoc they would cause, with the result that their aims were hopelessly engulfed by what followed. There are theories that they were islamicists, environmentalists, nihilists, even conceptual artists. Whoever they were, they had quietly slipped into jobs at banks and various financial institutions and established themselves as ordinary employees – until the signal came to unleash their plan. This was to commit themselves to impossible trading positions on the world's financial markets: positions which could result in only one thing: the collapse of the institutions for whom they worked. Few people ever understood the financial weapons which they employed, nor could have imagined what effect they would have. Nor, initially, could ordinary people have appreciated the effect that an attack on arcane global financial systems could have such an effect on their personal lives.

'For some hours, the attack came across as a piece of surreal entertainment. The sight of frantic, sweating bankers tearing out their hair, the odd one throwing himself from the building in which he worked, provoked almost a holiday spirit among ordinary people who felt themselves far removed from the mood swings of international finance. When the first bank failed it was almost seen as a joke. When the second and third went down people began to wonder. When five, ten, fifteen banks failed it was quite clear that the world's financial systems were under deliberate and sustained attack. There were confused smiles on the faces of ordinary people; a feeling of secret admiration for those who had pulled off the deed. Then came the realisation of what it meant for them personally. Markets had collapsed, investments had been lost. People with debts had found them suddenly magnified several hundred-fold. Wages went unpaid, bank accounts were frozen. The supply of money dwindled to virtually nothing. Overnight, all commerce was quickly reduced to bartering and promises.

'On its own, the attack could not have brought an end to the industrial age. The financial systems could have been reconstructed. Those who had lost out might have been compensated in some way. States possessed emergency powers to enable them to do these things. Yet no state could cope with the panic which followed. The banks and insurance offices were besieged by those who had lost their money. The public armed themselves with knives and clubs, visited their banks and demanded that the vaults be opened. Yet when this was done, the vaults were found to contain only token quantities of money. Bankers and their staff were seized. I witnessed one attack myself, in which a banker was taken by an angry mob and trussed up. What few notes and coins his bank was found to contain were not stolen: they were stuffed into his mouth. Choking, he was tossed into the river and drowned.

'Governments hatched emergency plans to print more money. But it was not enough to satisfy those who had been shocked by the failure of an economic system they did not even understand. These people didn't want to be put back at the mercy of big business. They didn't want to be trapped in cities with faltering food supplies and failing electricity systems. They hankered for the kind of security which an advanced industrial civilisation could not offer them. Their instinct was to head for the land, where they could run the soil between their fingers and survive upon their own efforts; however an impossible a dream it would prove to be.

'The point is that many people had negative feelings against the industrialised world; feelings which were horribly encouraged by the collapse of financial systems. The ultimate cause of the fall of the industrial age was a loss of faith. This was a gradual process which began at the peak the industrial age. The fathers and grandfathers of my generation, that is to say those who were born early in the industrial age, had always looked forward to better times. They had known hardship and disease, and believed these things to be conditions from which human ingenuity would one day lift them. Just look, they said, at what Man had already beaten: hunger, disease, world war. They still dreamed that industrialisation was taking the world on to better things. Human civilisation they saw as a small farmstead in the midst of some dark wood: a small piece of order within a mass of awfulness. The process of industrialisation they conceived as the business of winning a few more yards from the wilderness and bringing them to cultivation.

'My own generation thought very differently about industrial civilisation. It wasn't in the farmstead that we saw civilisation; it was in the wood. We viewed the activities of Man as interfering with the perfect lives of plants and creatures. Had you asked my grandfather what he understood by the word "industry", he would have said "hard work". Put the same word to my generation and we would have said "pollution". As one of the witnesses explained, we tended always to see the negative side: we thought of the creatures driven to extinction, the delicate balance of nature upset by thoughtless acts on our part. In the making of advanced industrial civilisation we saw a morality tale; we had abused the natural world, and therefore we must at some point be punished for what we had done.

'There were many – and I cannot exclude myself entirely – who found it hard to accept the ugliness created by the process of industrialisation. We would look at a motorway, a factory, the ravenous consumption of landscape by development and we heard ourselves muttering to ourselves: perhaps it would not be a bad thing if some day this could all be reversed and nature take charge once more. The destruction of the industrial age city was acted out in the cinema many times over: our civilisation consumed by fire, flood or pestilence. It was a vision which drew huge audiences. Having seen familiar landmarks razed from the Earth, we would leave the cinema in fright, though perhaps with a little hope in our hearts, too, because it satisfied us to think that the noisy, smoky, greedy places in which we lived might not be there to sully the planet for eternity.

'The terrorist attack on the banking system provoked a massive and terrible rejection of global capitalism and all that it was held to represent. The many and varied charges which had been laid at the door of multinational enterprises were repeated continuously and amplified many times over. Industrialisation, it was asserted, was laying waste to the environment, exploiting the poor, ruining our health and suppressing all whom it employed. It took several months for this ill-feeling to mutate into terror, but when it did nobody was safe.

'At the time, I was employed in market research for a company which sold chocolate snacks in brightly-coloured wrappers. This is not an occupation to which one is minded to admit these days. Many of those for whom I worked were tried and put to death on a charge of promoting obesity. After many threats, the company's annual general meeting was stormed and its directors seized. There was a brief trial at which they were accused and summarily convicted of ruining diets and greatly enfeebling the populace, all for their own profit – an "act of cynicism", as it was described at the time. The method of execution was especially cruel: they were force-fed with their company's own products before a jeering crowd. They were held down, while their mouths were wired open and chocolate was stuffed into them. Moaning and dribbling, they were made to admit their sin. But it made no difference: still the food was pushed into them until finally they drowned or were suffocated by the goo. Such was the atmosphere in the years of terror which followed the industrial age. It wasn't just the directors of chocolate companies who were subjected to terrible punishment. Senior staff of tobacco firms were locked into small chambers and asphyxiated with tobacco smoke. Motor manufacturers, whose roll of victims was huge, were either strapped into their cars and gassed or else tied to test rigs and had cars crashed into them, the crowds cheering as their bones were broken. There was great and perverse cruelty, which the perpetrators justified in the interests of making the punishment fit the crime.

'I survived the first wave of terror because I saw what was coming and switched sides. In the nervous months following the attacks on the banking system I gave up my job in marketing and took one at a university studying the ill-effects of obesity. I destroyed my previous work, so that my earlier role was concealed. Under interrogation I insisted that my purpose all along had been to expose the industry in which I worked for its evil intent. I am very sorry that some of my later work may have sent one or two confectioners to their deaths, but it was necessary for me to adopt such a position in order to survive.

'It is a great irony that when chocolate bars are discovered these days, they are, in spite of their staleness, treated as great delicacies. This is especially so among wealthy people of progressive mind, who seem not to care that their actions are contrary to their professed ideals.'

'If I could interrupt,' began one of the inquisitors. 'We appreciate you making to journey to see us, and sparing the time to make your statement. But there are things we do not fully understand. It seems that you reject the evidence of many witnesses to this inquiry, who have spoken at great length about the environmental degradation and the enfeeblement of the human body which they say occurred as a result of the processes of industrialisation. Do you mean to say that you reject the case that food was manufactured in the industrial age deliberately in order to fatten the people and so to cause their death for the perverse pleasure of those who made the food?'

'Methods were used to persuade the people to buy certain foods, but this did not amount to a conspiracy of the nature you describe, no.'

'But we have heard from a witness who herself used to work in a food factory, and she gives us her word that she was ordered to fill these foods with salt and sugar in order to create intolerable cravings in the people who bought them, and that as a result many people gained great weight and died, and that the directors of these companies were caught laughing and joking about those they had killed in this way. Are you to say that you reject this?'

'It was not in the interests of businesses to kill their customers. It is a fantasy to claim that they set out to do this. At the peak of the industrial age people were living longer and enjoying better health than they had ever done before and have ever done since. But this is forgotten. If you speak to young people these days it is clear that they believe people lived short and miserable lives back in the industrial age, and that by comparison now they live to ripe old ages.'

'But it is true!' cried a lady from the back of the room. 'Look, just look at the evidence.' And she waved a sheath of old newspaper clippings with headlines such as 'Tragic tot killed by bug in under-cooked burger' and 'Injection turned my son into a zombie'. 'Day after day these cases appeared. There is such a weight of them that you cannot dismiss them. Why were these people allowed to kill as they did?'

'It was part of the undoing of the industrial world that fear came to be used as a political tool,' I said. 'The industrial age was a time of unparalleled comfort, but I concede that it must not seem that way if you read cuttings from old newspapers. That is because the political leaders of the day, not to mention commercial concerns, realised that people can easily be manipulated when they are frightened. And, so easy was the transmission of information in those days, that people were very quickly and easily scared. There is far more misery these days; it is just that it does not get written down like it was then. That the industrialists purposely set out to kill is a myth, first told by powerful interests back in the industrial age, and magnified many times over by our current leaders in order to deflect attention from their own murderous habits.'

There was audible gasping, but the inquisitor went on: 'You appear now to be making wider assertions: that the real malice was not back in the industrial age; it is now. If that is your view you must explain it, because it runs so counter to the weight of evidence we have heard at this inquiry. What have you to say of the hundreds of people whom, as we have heard, have been killed by the tiny particles of asbestos which still drift in the air above every industrial age town? And those who have been killed by dioxins released by old rubbish dumps? The many thousands killed by drinking radioactive water from old nuclear power stations?'

'It is curious that the hazards of which you speak, like so many of the alleged hazardous legacies of the industrial age talked about these days, are invisible to the naked eye,' I said. 'I have seen people harmed by the detritus of the industrial age, such as those who have snagged their legs on old pieces of iron while hunting for rodents in long grass, but I believe the numbers who come to grief as a result of industrial effluent to be hugely exaggerated. In some cases they are entirely imagined.'

'Can you really mean this? We have heard, too, from witnesses who attest to the gross distortions of climate which have occurred as a result of global warming. We have heard from a witness who lost her entire family in raging floods in Greenwich, from a witness who himself lost a leg when a tree fell on him during a storm, and from a witness who was horribly burned by the sun and who as a result has been unable to sit down for several years. We have seen the evidence from many documentary sources that the weather did not used to be this foul before the change in climate at the end of the industrial age. Are you to say that you deny the weather has changed for the worse as a result of industrial activities?'

'We do not know, because nobody keeps records of the weather any more, but I cannot honestly say that the weather is worse now than it was back in the industrial age. It is just that people sense it is: every time we have a storm they pray for salvation, thinking that it is the wrath of God. They say He is returning to the Earth all the electricity generated back in the industrial age. They do not understand that there have always been thunderstorms.'

There was much protest from the audience at this. In an attempt to return order to the proceedings, the inquisitors allowed a young lady in a trouser suit and headscarf to make a point. 'But look here at the evidence,' she said, holding up a very dog-eared holiday brochure. 'Look, the pictures show bright sunshine, page after page. And yet the people in the pictures are not getting burned. This indicates quite clearly that the natural condition of the weather in those days was gentle sunshine, not the foul storms or the scorching sun rays which afflict us now.'

'You are being somewhat selective in the material which you have chosen to present to the inquiry,' I said.

The chief inquisitor leaned across his desk and looked me in the eye. 'But the deterioration in the climate is not just a tale told by people in this room,' he said. 'Why, we have heard evidence from several elderly people who remember that the hazards of global warming were much talked about back in the industrial age, too. Respected lawyers and physicians of the time have been quoted as lending their own considerable expertise. And these were people who might have been expected to support the industrial system! Surely you cannot deny the overwhelming evidence that industrial processes killed and maimed people in huge numbers.'

'As I have said, it is unfortunate that back in the industrial age fear came to be used as a powerful tool of politics and commerce. To sell suncream, it was necessary first to spread fear of the sun, with the implication that cosmic rays were becoming stronger and dangerous thanks to industrial pollution. To sell mineral water it helped to spread fear of contamination of the public water supply. I could go on. Those who promoted these hazards were motivated by the desire to sell their goods, and as such had a vested interest in the industrial age. Yet to many people this endless concentration on hazards helped to develop an ideology that was aggressively anti-industrial. Rather than enjoying the gadgets, machines, potions and lotions which were sold to them, people began to worry about them and to protest against them. At first these protests were pieces of carnival: protesters would climb the chimney of an incinerator and force its shut-down or they would tie themselves to trees about to be felled. But over time the protests became more serious, and more successful at disrupting the economy. The war against industrialisation turned into a war of attrition. It became all but impossible to conduct certain industries. Research into new medicines was halted by those who set out to free the animals on whom the drugs were tested. It became impossible to dump waste – of which small mountains were then generated – without encountering protestors who lay down in front of the wheels of rubbish lorries and threatened to make martyrs of themselves in the battle against environmental degradation. The costs of resisting these protests drove many companies to ruin, throwing their employees into unemployment.

'When people suffered misfortune, they looked to blame some industrial process or other. When they felt unwell, they looked for signs of poisoning, irradiation, physical assault. They sought lawyers to win them compensation. There came a point at which the fight against industrial goods became bigger business than the

production of them. Against this background it became impossible
to advance in many areas of technology. How could a genetic
engineer continue with his business when the greater part of
humanity believed him to be harbouring some crazed scheme to
pervert nature? Many such technologists braved the mob for a
while. But amid the wave of terror which followed the collapse of
the banking system most gave up their careers, or else were
horribly murdered.

   'Eventually, the anti-industrial fervour evolved into an all-
pervading doctrine: that the modern world was to blame for all
ills. It did not matter the nature of your complaint, the solution
was to be found in a simple way of life which rejected the
methods of the industrial age. We would think of the headache
we suffered every day on coming home from the office and
wonder: would our minds not be less fuddled if we were
employed in some more richly-rewarding manual task? We would
look with disgust at the drug addicts who were defiling the centres
of our cities and wonder, just wonder: would these wasters not be
brought to their senses if somehow we were to return to a state of
wholesome, pre-industrial existence?

   'Besides, we tired of industrial advance. There was a feeling of
excess about the industrial age, a sense of too-muchness, which
came to offend many. The production of industrial goods
proceeded eventually to chronic glut. The world, in short,
became too good at making things. There was great joy in the first
motor-car you owned; even more pleasure in the improved
model. But several models later, the feelings began to wear off.
The cars were too fast, too good at their jobs, so loaded with
gadgets that it would have been a lifetime's work to get to master
every function of which they were capable. At this point came
contempt. The vehicles were abused and quickly discarded. They
became novelties which were unable to hold their owners'
attentions for more than a few weeks. The market became
saturated, yet still the manufacturers continued to try to expand

the production of the vehicles, because expansion was the only business they knew. It was the same with all industrial goods. Little thought was given to the question: what happens when everyone in the world has two or three of these items in their possession? I will tell you what happened: consumers stopped consuming. They pared down their possessions with the aid of great bonfires or by discarding them in landfill sites. The great rubbish mountains which resulted from the disposal of industrial age goods have since been absorbed into the landscape, so seamlessly that few are aware of their origin. You can dig down into these mountains today and find astonishing things: discarded items which had barely been used. Some are still in their wrappings.

'They are the legacy of the industrial age. Within a few years there will be nobody left who remembers these times. This inquiry will eventually end. The causes and the effects of industrial world will be entirely lost. The history will be reduced entirely to myth. And all that will be left will be this mass of buried goods which occasionally will push its way to the surface; the earth an exhibition hall of lost dreams.

'I have nothing more to say. I have spent my last few years as a keeper of the museum of industrial history. But it is a battle which scholars are bound to lose. It is the legend-writers who are winning. Soon there will no longer be anybody alive who saw the industrial age. And forever after it will be seen as a time of dragons and demons.'

15

I have written down my evidence as I intended to give it, though in fact I was heckled throughout my time at the witness stand. My delivery was broken and I did not manage to say all that I wanted to say. It is possible that I did not even say all the things which I have related to you. For some time I continued above the chatter and protest, which the inquisitors seemed powerless to stop. But by the point that I have now reached, I could no longer make myself heard at all. I stopped speaking and stood before this crowd, awaiting the verdict of the mob.

I was expecting to be overwhelmed, if not murdered, but to my surprise after a few more moments of barracking the racket quickly died down. We were close to the scheduled end of the day's proceedings, and people were leaving. The men in smocks now numbered no more than a dozen. I was allowed to leave the stand in peace; except, that is, from an approach by a bright-eyed young man with shoulder-length hair who wanted to share with me his thoughts. 'Professor!' he called. 'It is all very well what you say, but have you not heard of the works of the evolutionary scientists?' I told him that of course I had, but that he had better be careful with whom he discussed them because in many places they would earn him a death sentence. 'I belong to a group which reads these works in secret,' he went on. 'We will not be put off studying them. It would do you good to look at them too, because it would at once become obvious to you why Man lost faith in industrial progress: it was an evolutionary response to the threat of self-destruction. Had we not rejected industrial methods it is quite obvious that we would no longer be here. What future had mankind once he had mastered the technology required to bring nuclear weaponry down to the price of a family car so that any malcontent and psychopath could afford one? None. None at all. We had to find a way of uninventing these devices and so we did: economic collapse. How could it have been any other way? It's been miserable these past few years, oh to be sure it has. But it was all for the good. That is the truth.' And with this he smiled and shuffled off into the crowds.

A feast had been arranged for that night: a celebration of what the organisers considered to be the imminent economic recovery, combined with an awards' ceremony which would honour those who were believed to be making the greatest contribution towards the restoration of industrial methods. No sooner had the crowds dispersed from the public inquiry than long tables were erected across the floor of the exhibition hall. They were laid with plastic cutlery – a great luxury, it was considered by the organisers – and adorned with fresh flowers. There is an abundance of these latter items in cities these days; old parks and gardens, though long neglected, flourish with flowers, many of whose names have been long-forgotten. Within half an hour – the staff taking much pride in the speed at which they prepared for the feast – I and a couple of hundred or so other guests were being led to our tables. The guests, I noticed, were mostly elderly: weathered men and women in threadbare suits who boasted of long-ended careers in finance, law, accountancy and other lost professions. There were civil servants, engineers with oily fingernails who had spent the day tending exhibits. Seated closer to the heads of the tables was a class of merchants: much younger men who spoke of their adventures at sea, the most vociferous of whom claimed to have a fleet of fifty yachts. They were observed, quite suspiciously, by several old figures who announced themselves as civil servants, one of whom told me he had made it his business to regulate these vessels. It was shameful, he said, the state in which some of them put to sea – people had drowned in the river not 100 yards from where we sat. 'It is a disgrace that there are no seaworthiness tests for vessels on the Thames,' he said. 'It must be put right and it will. We cannot tolerate the loss of life any longer.' There were tax-collectors – burly men, the lot, who told tales of violent clashes with adventurers in the suburbs: 'They cannot and they will not,' one said, 'get away with this trade in human flesh – untaxed.' There were gold-prospectors, pamphlet-writers, 'economic forecasters' who demanded to see the palms of your hands and to deliver their wisdom. But most conspicuously of all were a class of elderly women dressed in jewels, interspersed at the head of each table. They called themselves celebrities.

'Oh, no, I am nothing,' said one, whose hair was heavily dyed and powdered. 'I am just a minor celebrity. My work is nothing compared with the works of the great celebrities. You must, surely, have heard the stories of the African children who were starving – on the point of death – until visited by celebrities who touched their hands and brought them to their feet once more. It was astonishing what good works the great celebrities were able to perform, simply through the force of their personalities. Would that we had them among us now to make such a difference to the lives of the poor. It is obscene that people should be allowed to suffer as they do. It makes me so angry to see people dying of diseases which used to be cured by celebrities. But I believe the great celebrities will come among us again. The time is nearly here. Once more they will cure the sick and feed the hungry.'

The celebrities were feted by all, but unquestionably the principal guest was the king. He was an emaciated figure who but for the attention paid to him would have been inconspicuous. The moment he entered the hall, there were loud cheers and every-body stood up. He was shown to his table and, though he said little himself, he was soon seen to be listening intently to the organisers of the exhibition who were seated around him, all eager to catch his ear. Soon after the king's arrival, the food was served: burgers made from loosely-bound minced meat, probably rat, cat or dog, enclosed in paper wrappings and accompanied by potatoes fried to a dark crisp. Rough-tasting wines and beers, fermented and brewed from whatever came to hand, flowed freely. After a tense beginning there developed an atmosphere of some merri-ment. Comedians plied their trade between the tables, telling tales and jokes which they had picked up from old books and which they clearly did not understand, in common with many of the guests. But the guests laughed loudly all the same. The food was plentiful, and grease was soon dribbling down diners' chins: there was no shame in this sight, for it has become a virtue to be seen to eat well. Everyone had a tale to tell: of distant places they had visited in their youth, of things they used to own, of how much they used to fit into their day, of the great organisations which they used to head. They spoke warmly of huge crowds in which they had once found themselves: 'You see the people in this hall? They are nothing,' said one white-haired man enthusiastically. 'There were ten times, twenty times this number on the trains every morning of the week. To feel yourself part of this great moving mass of humanity, there was nothing like it. There is no feeling which you can experience these days which can compare in any way.' Another said: 'I remember the great awards cere-monies for actuaries; which in their heyday were attended by over a thousand people. They have become very sparsely-attended events in recent years and the meals have become poor, but this reminds me so much of the atmosphere of the old days.' Then he opened his jacket to reveal an array of clip-on name badges which he wore like military medals but which had been less gloriously won attending conferences and awards' ceremonies of actuaries.

As the meal progressed I got talking to my neighbour: a silvery-haired lady with rings around her eyes which it seemed may have been caused by wearing spectacles, though she seemed to have taken the decision not to wear them in public. 'The exhibition is so exciting because it has been such a long and deep recession,' she said. 'But my business is picking up by the day and I can foresee that soon I will be as busy as I ever was. Who knows, it may then be possible to push up my fees again and to restore the way of life that I lost. I have only been at this exhibition three hours, and already I have found a client: a poor fellow who singed his hands on a steam engine and has had them bandaged. There will be little trouble in winning him some good coinage in compensation. The owner of the machine should have taken a lot more care than he did. Ah, what good business it is to be a mediator! And what benefit to society will come from these matters. And it is all because we have taken the trouble to maintain the integrity which the corrupt lawyers of old were lacking.'

It was two hours before one of the organisers rose to his feet and appealed for silence. There were speeches to be made, prizes to be given. 'I must first thank you all for attending,' he began. 'You have come from all over the country. I know that it has not been easy for you, but your presence here puts lie to the idea that Britain has become a land of poverty and savages. It is a story maliciously put about that no man may safely travel about the country any longer. In fact, it is quite clear that the industrial system is open for business once more and that the confidence which had been lost is being quickly restored. Let us, for once, hear the good news. Trade in herrings, up 15 per cent this year. Prices of property, doubled at least. The number of steam engines operational in London, up from nothing last year to four this year. These are the statistics you rarely hear from the doom-mongers. There are people who will tell you industrial civilisation is finished. Well, I say to those people: come to London and see the truth laid out before your eyes!' For this, the organiser was warmly cheered, with just one or two voices of dissent. 'I know some who weren't so lucky in trying to reach this exhibition,' said one of these voices quietly. 'They had their throats cut at Iver Heath and their bodies were displayed by the roadside for all to see. I had known them in Oxford and I recognised them from what the crows had left of their corpses. The speaker is a fool to say what he does. We are encircled by savages and we are in great danger.' For this he was loudly hissed by most of the dinner guests within earshot.

The chief organiser, who had not heard, went on: 'The past twenty years have been extremely difficult. It would be silly to try to deny that. But wherever one looks, it is quite clear that there has been a great revival in the industrial system. If the recovery in the economy can be sustained I have no doubt that within a few years the problem of production will once again be solved and there will be ample food, drink and entertainment for all. It is my hope, and I suspect the hope of all of you assembled here this evening, that we will learn from the cruel recession through which we have just been, that lessons will be learned and that we will be able to adjust our political and economic structures so that the same tragedy will not strike future generations.

'Before I go on, we are of course indebted to our helpers. . .' And he went on for some time thanking the men and women, alive and dead, who had had a hand in the staging of the exhibition. I came to understand that the event had been several years in gestation. Sombrely, he told of workers who had fallen from great heights, been singed with steam or had been lacerated by the snapping of the long leather belts which transferred power from the steam engine to the individual contraptions on display in the exhibition hall. 'They died in glory. They made the supreme sacrifice in the great struggle against ignorance,' the chief organiser went on. 'It is up to us to carry on the work, and prove that they did not die in vain.' He then came to present the awards. There was a medal for a man who had resurrected an old printing press and so managed to print the programmes for the exhibition. There was an honour for a man who had restored several old bicycles, which were now being used by staff to move rapidly among the exhibits. There were prizes for bankers who had relearned the art of lending money, a very special award for an economist who had produced charts forecasting economic growth of 15 per cent every year for the next decade so that by the year 2065 the economy would finally have been restored to its peak. But the main prize was awarded to an aged man with long white hair who had spent the dinner sketching on a table cloth to the fawning admiration of all around him. It became clear that he had adopted the name 'Leonardo'.

'More than any other man alive, Leonardo has been responsible for assembling the marvellous collection of exhibits which we see before us today,' began the chief organiser. 'He has produced machines capable of cleaning the floors, of washing the tablecloths, of cooking the food that we are privileged to be eating this evening. He has produced a weaving machine and a threshing machine. It was he, too, who instigated the rail service between London Bridge and the exhibition hall: a facility which has not been seen in this country for many years. But above all it is he who invented the aeroplane which has been flying above our heads yesterday afternoon and which, once some teething troubles have been eliminated, will be carrying passengers across the Atlantic. There is, beyond question, no man alive who can claim to be playing a bigger role in the rekindling of industrial civilisation. Leonardo, we salute your enterprise, praise your courage, pay homage to your skill and intelligence. . . .'

Much later, in very different surroundings, I managed to speak to 'Leonardo'. I never did learn his real name, but I did discover a little of his history which he told me with great candour. 'I was a curator,' he said. 'I worked in several of the museums, but mostly the science museum, as it was then known. I knew the exhibits by heart. I had looked over them for several years. I had oiled them.

I knew how they worked. I knew where they still were. I knew my way into the building, which has been abandoned for many years. It was not until recently, when I learned of this exhibition and heard of the prizes available for investors, that it occurred to me how valuable those exhibits could be. Most of the goods which have been left over from the late industrial age are useless to us now. They are beyond our comprehension. Their method of working is lost in their silicon chips. But the older contraptions: they are a different story. With a little instruction any man can operate these.'

Leonardo never did get his award. While the chief organiser was making his speech, there began a commotion. I looked one way, and then the other. Nobody really knew which way to look. The racket was coming from all around us. It was a ripping sound, followed by shouting. Dozens of men dressed in overalls had cut their way through the skin of the building and were advancing upon us. There was nowhere for us to go. The few dinner guests who did try to make an escape were beaten savagely with clubs. The rest of us remained frozen at our tables and allowed ourselves to be captured.

The invaders made us stand up and strip off our outer layers of clothing, so that we were left shivering in the cool breeze which was by now blowing through the building. They checked us for weapons, snatching the plastic knives which a few guests had picked up in self-defence. We were then bound with rope, and tied together. We were slowly led from the building, our progress halted by guests who had gone weak at the knees and who had slumped to the ground; among them were several of the celebrities. The fallers were beaten with clubs and leather belts until they made some effort to get up.

It became clear that the invaders had a leader: a thick-set man with a grey beard, dressed in a long, roughly-woven shawl. Only when he spoke did I recognise him. 'Take them to the Tower!' bawled Julius Holder, as fellow invaders yanked on the ropes to speed us up. We were led through the broken walls of the dome and led the short distance to the riverside. There, we were forced into barges. One prisoner tried to escape by leaping overboard. But he was still constrained by his ropes and fell headlong into the water, where the invaders held him for several minutes while he thrashed about for his life. By the time he was finally lifted out of the water he had given up the struggle; his eyes were rolling and his mouth hanging open as he was dumped back in the boat. 'Did the authorities not make the perimeter secure?' asked the mediator to whom I had been sitting at dinner. 'It is a terrible oversight. They will pay for this. I will make sure of that.'

When the boats were full they were pushed out into the river by the invaders and slowly rowed across the river to what I knew to be the Isle of Dogs. The journey was prolonged, complicated by the heavy listing of the boat. For some time it seemed that we would be washed downstream, but the invaders forced their prisoners to join in with the rowing, and we began to make progress to the other bank. We were 50 yards from the shore when one of the smaller vessels began to tip. There was no stopping it: it capsized, tipping its passengers, screaming, into the cool water. Some simply disappeared, small circles of silent froth being the only sign of where they had sunk. Others bobbed about for a bit. Several began to swim away. Others engaged in fighting their captors. All were left to fend for themselves as the remaining boats continued on their faltering journey to the far bank. When we arrived, we looked back to see that the dome had been set alight. Its grubby skin was being consumed quickly by vast, crackling flames. Within an hour or so the frame of the building had collapsed, too: turned inwards to create the shape of a giant, smouldering doughnut. Horrid acrid smoke was to linger for days.

We landed on an old slipway and were marched along dark streets and docksides. Our captors lit flaming torches to guide our way between the tall buildings, which were still remarkably intact from the industrial age. Along the way we heard, though we

could not see, small scuffles to either side of us. It seemed that the
Progressive forces had only captured this part of London in recent
hours and had yet to make it fully secure, though the resistance
was light. Every so often there would be a commotion, followed
by the sickening sound of a man being punched and beaten. Once
or twice we heard a loud splash as troublesome captives were
tossed into the old docks.

We were forced to march on until we came to three vast tower
blocks. Around the central block vast numbers of Progressive
forces were standing guard, armed with great knives and swords: a
strange mixture of catering knives from the industrial age and
ancient weapons presumably recovered from museums. At this
point we were stopped, and examined individually. Each prisoner
was asked for his name, then pulled and shoved up the steps
leading to the doors of the tower. Eventually, it came to my turn.
I had the honour of being questioned by Julius Holder himself.

When he saw my face, he smirked. 'Professor, we have met
before,' he said. 'I think you remember the warnings that I issued
then. Is there anything you wish to say?' I spat on the ground and
uttered: 'You are barbarians, the lot of you!'. It seemed to annoy
Holder, who said sharply: 'I want him taken to the very top.
Charge him at once with unsustainable activities.'

It was an hour or so before I reached the uppermost storey. The
lifts no longer functioned, and the only way up was via the stairs.
The ascent began in silence, though after ascending a dozen
storeys or so two of the four guards who were accompanying me
decided that they were no longer needed. Once they had gone,
the remaining two began to talk. They told me of how they had
marched to London, a journey which had taken several days.
There had been upwards of two thousand men, all gathered from
Cambridge or from taverns along the way. They had come down
the Lea Valley, meeting scarcely any resistance. They had
expected a battle, and it seemed they were a little disappointed
that they did not get one. Some of the fighters had become so

pent up with aggression that they had slaughtered at whim the few wretches whom they had encountered. While the majority of the men had marched on Central London, several hundred had remained in the suburbs to consolidate the territory. Battles had been fought with wandering tribes in Hackney and Clapton. Survivors had been captured and put to work.

Before he had left Cambridge, it emerged, Julius Holder had declared himself the provisional leader of all England, with the title Lord Protector of the Environment. He and his accomplices had told tall stories about retrograde forces in London who had resurrected old machinery and were sucking the oxygen from the sky. If they were not stopped, Holder's bullies had been telling every man from Cambridge to London, it would not be long before men would suffocate. The population would succumb to allergies and cancers. Men would be enslaved in offices. Given these grim warnings, it proved easy to raise a force in defence of Progressive values. It was not that Holder wished to travel, it was asserted. In future he would not do so; it would not be necessary to do so. In future, no man would travel far from his village, nor eat food grown outside it. But it was impractical to impose these rules while the country was still in a state of counter-revolution. When industrialisation was finally defeated, Holder would return to Cambridge and live his life there; others would return to their villages and remain in them.

When we reached the 30th storey, I looked out over the ruins of London. They were lit by shafts of moonlight which had found gaps between the iron-grey clouds. The taller of the two guards looked out too and told me earnestly: 'One day, there will be nothing of this city left. It will be wiped from the map. Its depravity and its low customs will be gone. In its place will be a landscape of fields and villages, none of them numbering more than 300 souls. There will be no machinery, no concrete, no steel. This is our dream, and it will be achieved sooner than you imagine. Once the trials have concluded, work will begin. These

buildings have stubbornly resisted decay. But they will go. They
have fatal weaknesses. We know how to bring them down.'

'And the people?' I asked.

'The criminals will be dispensed with. The rest will be dispersed
to villages. There will be no coercion in this, of course. There will
be no need for it. The people will not need encouragement to
settle into a life of harmony with nature. It is in our blood. It is
just that that our instincts have been perverted by years of
industrialisation. But once freed from this oppressive system,
reversion to the natural order will be rapid, aided in some cases by
a brief programme of re-education. Within a few years we will
have created an Environment to last many thousands of years. The
world will settle down for ever after into a state of everlasting
Progress.'

I could barely stand up by the time we reached the top storey of
the tower. I could feel my heart beating loudly and irregularly.
My knees had weakened to the point at which I could no longer
support myself without the aid of my guards. Half an hour earlier
the guards would have dragged me, but now they seemed to take
pity on me and carried me the last few yards into a large open-plan
office. The air was frigid and gusty. The wind tore through what
had once been a large open-plan office, finding its way in through
the many broken windows, whose frames vibrated to create a
nerve-racking hum. The office was still fitted out with swivel
chairs and large plastic tables. I was laid down on one of these, my
leg pressed hard against the remains of a computer. There, I settled
into a fitful sleep.

I awoke halfway through the night to find that the office was
filling up with other prisoners, many of them squealing and
sobbing. By the first break of daylight the sounds of protest had
decayed to a little moaning and snoring. I awoke a second time to
be offered a little brackish water and a dry biscuit. Later that day,
our situation became clear: we were all to be tried before a body
which we learned was called The Grand Council on Climate

Change and Sustainable Agriculture. But before our trial could begin, we would be put to work. The fit and able were roped together and taken down to nearby parks and gardens which had been commandeered for the purposes of cultivation. It was pitiful to watch them several hundred feet below, breaking up the soil with their bare hands. The Progressive foremen had not yet discovered that these small patches of green were built atop the concrete roofs of underground car parks and the like, and had soil just a few inches deep. Food, it later became clear, was being brought in by cattle train from Essex. This transportation of food, it was explained, was of course just a temporary measure and would be halted as soon as the revolution had been won.

Myself, I have never left the upper storey of the tower. Soon after my arrival, I developed a chest infection which I was not expected to survive and which may well kill me yet. I have been through such bouts of delirium and pain that often I hope to expire before I am committed for trial. There is a rumour in any case – not discouraged by the guards – that I will be made an example of: that I am considered to be too old and too immersed in the history of industrialisation to be suitable for re-education. My fate is to be hanged, and sentence will be carried out when – or if – I am well enough to be taken downstairs. Already, so report the prisoners who have been taken downstairs for the purpose of labouring, several dozen men have been executed, their bodies left swinging from hastily-erected scaffolds at the foot of the tower. They have not been cut down, but have been left for the benefit of scavenging birds: in particular the great ravens which now soar over London. Among the Progressive forces, I am told, there is a debate over what should be done with the bodies of those executed. Some have suggested burial in order to enrich the ground, but others have argued that burial is unnatural; that the bodies of animals are designed to fall to the ground and be devoured by scavenging beasts there. This latter argument, for the moment, has won the day. It will take many years – perhaps centuries – of typhoid for the Progressives to relearn from first principles the causes and sources of human disease.

I cannot guess when, if ever, the wealth and wisdom of the industrial age will return. Enlightenment, at best, can be but a faint speck in the distance. There will be dark ages first. My consolation is that my guards will inevitably be wrong. The furniture of the industrial age cannot be wiped from the Earth as easily as they imagine. Long after the papers have rotted and the redundant machinery has rusted there will still be traces of what once stood here: girders of fallen buildings poking from the undergrowth, hard surfaces of roads beneath the weedy turf, indentations of the Earth where some sort of industrial activity once went on. There will always be these signs. But what will they mean to people? Will they be treated as mere obstacles or will they arouse the curiosity of those who live among them? Perhaps in hundreds of years' time a hunter-gatherer will chance upon a relict and just wonder: was there anything which preceded the state of enduring Progress in which he lives? From his moment of wonderment there might just grow a collective inquiry into human history. The whole thing might be pieced together once more: the lives, the customs and the achievements of the industrial age. It is possible, even probable. But for the moment the lights are going out. Progressive Man does not wish to be bothered by his past; he wishes only to forge his communion with nature.

My days are spent gazing out over this great city, remembering the noise and the energy of the place half a century ago. How ironic that at the time so many of us thought the city – its business, its shops, its roads, its trains, its rhythms – to be mundane! How differently we would have behaved had we known it was going to end like this, and so soon. Look out from this tower at night and you can see, not the lines of sodium lamps which used to march off into the suburbs, but dozens of small fires. They are lit by nomads for the purposes of cooking and keeping warm. Sometimes it is possible to imagine what the Progressives wish to see: London before London was ever there. At this point, I close my eyes, retreat to my memories and pray that at some distant time hence my bones might be discovered, and give an archaeologist some small clue as to the great, if troubled, civilisation which once had one of its cities on this spot.